THE NATURE OF NUMBER

An Approach to Basic Ideas
of Modern Mathematics

By

ROY DUBISCH

ASSOCIATE PROFESSOR OF MATHEMATICS
FRESNO STATE COLLEGE

THE RONALD PRESS COMPANY ⸲ NEW YORK

4

Library of Congress Catalog Card Number: 52–6182

PRINTED IN THE UNITED STATES OF AMERICA

TO

MY PARENTS

PREFACE

Every nonfictional book has a certain ready-made audience composed of persons who have had some previous pleasant contact with the subject treated. And those persons who have always enjoyed mathematics will, I hope, find their interest in the subject renewed, and their knowledge of it advanced, by this book. But I shall count my efforts more successful if I may also attract those readers to whom mathematics has always been a bugaboo, who have built up a resistance to the understanding of it, or who have always thought of it as being as dead as the Latin language.

To those people who have never been able to stand mathematics, I should like to remark that their dislike may have been formed early in life by school experiences. Many aversions to history have been built up by teachers who taught history by riding herd over a collection of dates, and to geography by a method of presentation in which drill on the capitals of the forty-eight states formed a significant part. And if the above examples seem extreme, consider grammar-school arithmetic with its twin tormentors—the addition and multiplication tables.

There is some chance, however, of history and geography's receiving a better treatment in later schoolwork. But mathematics remains in a comatose condition all through grammar school. All too often, in fact, it barely comes to life in high-school or in freshman and sophomore college work. Thus, even in college, the student frequently still does not come into contact with living mathematics—the mathematics of the contemporary mathematician. Instead, he largely studies formal manipulation, useful in solving problems of physics and engineering but not useful in fostering an understanding of modern mathematics which is so highly unmanipulational.

For real mathematics is a constantly expanding subject in which *ideas* and not manipulations play the dominant role. These ideas are the subject matter of this book. Some of them will help to clothe the mechanics of ordinary arithmetic with real meaning. Others will deal with new and startling types of numbers which the scientists of today need for their work.

Now there is no way I know of to make mathematics altogether easy—particularly the mathematics of today. But I am convinced that a considerable part of the difficulty that attends a student's first study of advanced mathematics in graduate school is due to his lack of realization of the abstractions underlying even very elementary mathematics. For, again, most of the emphasis in grammar-school, high-school, and undergraduate college mathematics is upon the applications of the subject matter. Applications of mathematics include, of course, the usual word problems of algebra. But deeper than this, the symbols in elementary mathematics are taken to represent numbers, which in turn are thought of as standing for the amount or measure of some physical quantity.[1] And this, as I hope to show, is exactly what is *not* done in modern mathematics.

The main object of this book, then, is to give the reader a good idea of the kind of problems that mathematicians are working on today, not just what they have worked on in the past. Although in theory it is possible to go to this advanced work without any great reliance on the reader's previous mathematical background, in practice such a procedure is difficult even for many beginning graduate students. Hence my first efforts will go into the making of "easy mathematics hard." That is, I shall go back to the very primitive ideas of

---

[1] In fact, a common definition of mathematics is "That science treating of the exact relations existing between quantities or magnitudes . . ." (*Webster's Collegiate Dictionary*, 5th ed.).

counting and ordinary arthimetic and reveal there the abstractions which lead to modern mathematics. In doing this I
restrict myself to only a small part of mathematics in order to
encompass the range from prehistoric times to contemporary
research.

At this stage of the preface for books of this type it is common to assure the reader that no great amount of mathematical background is needed—and to this sentiment I echo
agreement. An ability to follow a logical argument is the
essential prerequisite for this book—this, and a mind open to
new ideas.

While I shall follow a historical pattern in the development, the stress of the book is not on formal history. As a
matter of fact, in certain places the history will be idealized
in order to make it follow a more logical pattern! In this connection I may remark that I shall adopt the point of view that
mathematics is *invented* rather than *discovered*—the Platonic
idealist may substitute "discover" for "invent" wherever the
latter occurs! Also, in what history is presented, I shall confine myself to a discussion of the mathematics of Western
Europe, leaving out any mention of the Oriental mathematics
which did not contribute to the development of Western
mathematics.

In order to avoid an excess of technical terms, I have been
forced from time to time into mathematical colloquialisms.
Likewise, in order to avoid an excess of qualifying clauses,
some statements are made which need, for preciseness, additional restrictions. So I have added a few technical footnotes
and a technical appendix to clarify these points. A reading of
these footnotes and the appendix is *not* necessary for a good
general understanding of the subject but will help those who
wish to go further into it.

A final word concerning the problems which are listed at
the end of each chapter and for which completely worked-
out answers are provided at the end of the book. In rereading

one version of the manuscript, I felt that more illustrative examples were needed. Rather than delay the line of development in the text, however, I have put them at the end of each chapter. Some readers (I hope, many) will be interested in testing their understanding of what they have read by trying these problems. On the other hand, those who have failed to grasp an abstract concept through lack of sufficient examples may find that the reading of the solutions of these problems may be just what they need in order to master the concept.

I am indebted to many books—especially in the early chapters. Most of them are listed in the concluding bibliography. In particular, however, I want to acknowledge a debt of inspiration to the masterful writings of E. T. Bell whose many publications have been a constant source of stimulation to me. For aid in making the manuscript readable, I thank Arnold Biella. For acting patiently as a typical reader and for constant encouragement, my deepest thanks go to my wife, Joyce.

To conclude with the customary quotation, I select the remarks of the reviewer of a vital book appearing in 1888 as appropriate to my point of view:

> There is probably no other science which presents such different appearances to one who cultivates it and one who does not, as mathematics. To [the noncultivator] it is ancient, venerable, and complete; a body of dry, irrefutable, unambiguous reasoning. To the mathematician, on the other hand, his science is yet in the purple bloom of vigorous youth, everywhere stretching out after the "attainable but unattained," and full of the excitement of nascent thoughts; its logic is beset with ambiguities, and its analytic processes, like Bunyan's road, have a quagmire on one side and a deep ditch on the other, and branch off into innumerable bypaths that end in wilderness.[2]

---

[2] C. H. Chapman, *Bulletin of the New York Mathematical Society*, 2, 1892, p. 61. (This and many other quotations concerning mathematics and mathematicians were collected by R. M. Moritz in his *Memorabilia Mathematica*, New York: Macmillan Co., 1914.)

May some of the "purple bloom" appear in what follows—but I will try to avoid, in this elementary treatment, the quagmires and ditches. Above all, I hope that we shall not end in a wilderness!

R. D.

Fresno, California
February, 1952

ACKNOWLEDGMENTS

The author wishes to thank the following authors and publishers whose works he has used in the preparation of this book:

C. J. Keyser, *Mathematics* (1907), Columbia University Press; D. E. Smith and L. C. Karpinski, *The Hindu-Arabic Numbers* (1911), Ginn & Co.; Bertrand Russell, *Introduction to Mathematical Philosophy* (1930), The Macmillan Co., by permission; E. T. Bell, *The Magic of Numbers* (1946), McGraw-Hill Book Co., Inc.; A. N. Whitehead, *Introduction to Mathematics* (1911), in the Home University Library, Oxford University Press; Richard Courant and H. E. Robbins, *What Is Mathematics?* (1941), Oxford University Press; E. T. Bell, *Men of Mathematics* (1940), Simon & Schuster, Inc.; Bertrand Russell, *Mysticism and Logic* (1929), W. W. Norton & Co., Inc.

CONTENTS

THE NATURE OF
NUMBER

Chapter 1

COUNTING FROM ONE TO A GOOGOL [1]

M ANY children can count up to ten or beyond as an
exercise in memory, comparable to the learning of a
nonsense jingle, before they have a clear idea of what the
words "two", "three", etc. are used for. Such a procedure is
quite contrary to the evolution of the counting process. Or,
to put it another way, although the human embryo, as biolo-
gists have shown, goes through the successive evolutionary
stages before assuming its final form, the child's development
of a number sense does *not* follow the pattern of evolutionary
development. That is, in the language of the evolutionist,
mathematical ontogeny frequently does not recapitulate
mathematical phylogeny—a statement the truth of which will
be repeatedly demonstrated in the first chapters of this book.

In considering this evolution, note first that there are actually two distinct concepts of, say, the number 3. It may
stand on the one hand for the measure of the size of a collection of objects, or it may stand for the order of an item in a
collection as the number 3 is reached by counting 1, 2, 3. It
may be difficult for a contemporary adult to capture the distinction between these two concepts, but it is, for the child
and primitive man, a very vivid one. For example, present
the child of four with the figures on page 4 and ask if
there are the same number of faces as houses. The chances
are that the child will not answer yes until he has counted

---

[1] The word *googol*, according to Kasner in his (and Newman's) *Mathematics and the Imagination,* was invented by his nine-year-old nephew to
designate the large number 1 followed by a hundred zeros. The word seems
to have filled a definite gap in our language and is being increasingly used.

one, two, three, four with *both* sets of objects. He, in effect, reverses the historical development, for an untutored but intelligent adult savage would say that there is the same number without being able to count at all. The savage child, on the other hand, presumably would not be able to reach any decision. This illustrates, on the one hand, the use of a mechanical artifice (in this case, the counting process) to help out the reasoning process and, on the other hand, the fact that this mechanical artifice blurs the distinction between two concepts (4 as a name to describe the "size" of a set and 4 as the successor of 3). These double-edged devices will be met with many times, and it is the difficult task of the mathematics teacher to sharpen one edge of the blade while dulling the other.

Let us now imagine a primitive man with a number of sticks to which he desires to affix flint heads. At his level of mathematical knowledge our savage has only a vague concept of the number of sticks (if forced to speak about them he may say that he has "many"), but he does know that he must match the flint heads with the sticks—and does so. Storing the completed spears away in a safe place, he wishes to brag about his day's work as the tribe gathers around the evening fire. Without any spoken language at all our friend could imitate the making of a spear and then, to indicate the magnitude of his achievement, match in his audience's mind the number of spears with marks on the ground or extended fingers. Note that the word *number*, which connotes in most modern minds a counting process, has not been used, and yet our ancestors were satisfied that a clear indication of their comrade's achievement (or boasting prowess) had been given.

A matching process can certainly suffice for indicating the size of a small collection of objects.[2] As language developed, however, the idea of "three" as the measure of the size of a collection of objects of which a typical "model" is shown below began to be confused with the idea of "three" as the

successor of "two", where "two" is the successor of "one". Theoretically, one can imagine a culture in which there are words for the idea of "three", "four", etc. as descriptions of the total number of objects in a collection but in which there is no counting process in which "four" follows "three". Actually, however, no such culture has been found. Thus, almost all the primitive tribes investigated by anthropologists which have not yet reached the stage of finger counting have a number vocabulary consisting of the words "one", "two"— and "many" to indicate any size beyond two.

To emphasize once more the importance of the *procession* of numbers as contrasted with the *individual* numbers in the development of a fluent number sense, study the collections of dots in (a), (b), (c), (d), and (e) below:

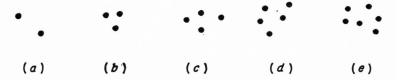

(a) (b) (c) (d) (e)

[2] Note, by the way, that finger counting was prevalent in Europe as late as the sixteenth century.

Without counting in sequence, give the number of dots in each set. The average person can comprehend (not count) one, two, three, or four dots (or teacups, children, etc.); but if he is honest about it, he will confess an inability to state the number of dots in a larger collection. There are certain apparent exceptions to this statement. For example, you might say that you can see at a glance, without counting, that there are nine dots in the collection below. An honest intro-

$$\begin{matrix} \bullet & \bullet & \bullet \\ \bullet & \bullet & \bullet \\ \bullet & \bullet & \bullet \end{matrix}$$

spection, however, would undoubtedly reveal that you are unconsciously using groupings by three's (which involves counting) in obtaining the result. Furthermore, familiarity with certain special sets of objects, such as five fingers, six place settings at a table, etc., and certain symmetrical arrangements, would give anyone a pseudo extension of this ability.

We have now reached the stage where the reader should be conscious of the idea of what mathematicians call a *cardinal* number as contrasted with an *ordinal* number. A cardinal number implies matching rather than counting—as did our spear maker—while an ordinal number implies a counting process. As suggested, the ideas are closely connected, and even primitive people have been found with a quite advanced counting process (as will be described later). Actually, the distinction is not of prime importance for our purposes, and only a very brief description of these concepts has been given here to indicate how early in mathematics do subtleties and fine distinctions arise that are completely glossed over in our usual introduction to arithmetic. In fact, throughout the training that the future mathematician receives along with those who are interested mainly in applications of mathematics, these fine points of arithmetic,

algebra, etc. are often grossly neglected. A certain amount
of neglect is obviously necessary (otherwise, for example,
schools would have to delay instruction in arithmetic until
maturity). But when the prospective mathematician begins
his own specialized training he is suddenly asked to emphasize those very points which he had previously ignored. This
is often a very difficult thing to do.

Although there is an interesting development of the ideas
of ordinal and cardinal numbers, I am more concerned here
with another hidden abstraction which underlies the "obvious" idea of a whole number such as "two" and for which
again we have historical and psychological evidence. This is
the distinction, say, between the abstract idea of "two" and
the idea of "two" chairs, apples, men, etc. The latter idea, of
course, is the more primitive of the two, and, as Bertrand
Russell says, "It must have required many ages to discover
that a brace of pheasants and a couple of days were both
instances of the number two". To which remark E. T. Bell
adds, "And it took some twenty-five centuries of *civilization*
to evolve Russell's own logical definition of 'two' or of any
cardinal number . . .".

As historical evidence of the inability of our primitive
ancestors to conceive of the abstract idea of number, consider
the Tsimshian language of a British Columbia tribe as re-
ported by the anthropologist Franz Boas. He found seven
distinct sets of number words: one for flat objects and ani-
mals, one for round objects and divisions of time, one for
men, one for long objects, one for canoes, one for measures,
and one (probably a later development) for counting when
no definite object is referred to. Likewise, as pointed out
before, the child just learning to count also does not recog-
nize the general character of a whole number.

What, then, is the modern point of view of a whole number or, as mathematicians usually refer to it, a *positive
integer*? Far from trying to hide the abstract nature of the

number "two", the modern mathematician takes pride in the fact that it is an abstraction which may, if desired, be applied to any number of concrete realities. Thus when we learn that $2 + 2 = 4$ we have eliminated the need for a recount when two chairs are carried into a room already containing two chairs as well as when a double visitation of twins occurs. In fact, modern mathematics may be said to have begun with the realization that abstraction and the use of undefined terms were virtues rather than vices—and these virtues will be fully extolled later.

In the meantime, consider how the cave man's collection of uncoordinated grunts developed into a systematic series of words which enable us to speak glibly today about such large numbers as the distance to the nearest star, the number of molecules in a quart of water, and the size of the national debt. For although the primary interest of this book is the *ideas* behind mathematical concepts, it would be very shortsighted indeed to ignore questions of notation and procedure entirely. These are not only inventions of great ingenuity but they are of inestimable value in enabling the mind to grasp the abstract concepts involved (although, alas, sometimes obscuring the concepts by substituting facile ability in manipulation for understanding). To illustrate this point with a familiar example, contrast the difficulties of computation with Roman numerals as compared with the ordinary (Hindu-Arabic) numerals. Developing a simple and easily remembered rule for multiplication in Roman numerals is quite impossible; hence the abacus remained a necessary tool for even short computations so long as Roman numerals were in common use.

Returning, then, to our "saber-tooth curriculum", suppose that a counting process for small numbers has been developed but that primitive men are puzzled by the seeming necessity of having *unrelated* names for each number. For the flocks of sheep, collections of shells, etc. are becoming quite large, and the resulting memory burden involved in counting these collections becomes intolerable. That is, while *today* we do not object too much to learning ten distinct and unrelated words with which to count our fingers, we are glad that (after a brief period of irregularity with eleven, twelve, and thirteen—to be discussed later) we can continue on our toes with *four*teen, *fif*teen, *six*teen, and so on. But it was this device which was first lacking in the counting process.

The scene is now set for the introduction of the capital idea of having groupings of 10, 100, 1000, $\cdots$ (or, as described later, of 5, 25, 125, $\cdots$ or 20, 400, 8000, $\cdots$). Thus the number vocabulary is now one, two, $\cdots$, nine, ten, and then ten-one, ten-two, ten-three, $\cdots$, ten-nine, two tens, two tens – one, two tens – two, etc. Clearly, however, a somewhat *better* form of our counting process has been described than actually exists. For the words for several numbers—11, 12, and 13, in particular—do not follow such a pattern very clearly. Such exceptions, however, are due to changes in language. For example, "eleven" is the modern form of the Anglo-Saxon word *endlufon* meaning "one left over" (i.e., ten plus one). Similarly, twelve is from *twelf* (two left), while thirteen is from *threotyne*, "three (plus) ten". In fourteen to nineteen the "teen" stands for (plus) ten, while twenty is from *twentig*, "twain ten" or two tens.

As we proceed up the number scale, the words become more regularized, with seventy being very close to seventens, while for 1224 we read "one thousand, two hundred, and twenty four" in a very descriptive fashion. Thus our number vocabulary today consists essentially of the words one, two, . . ., nine, ten, plus words for the "powers" of 10: 10^2 is a hundred, 10^3 is a thousand, . . ., 10^{100} is a googol. All other numbers are then named by combining these words according to a definite rule.

Such a systematic way of proceeding in the counting of numbers is an indispensable part of any extended system of calculation and is known to have been used in essentially the way we use it today by the Babylonians and Chaldeans in one of the primeval seats of human society—the fertile valley of the Euphrates and the Tigris. This is *not* to say that the Babylonians (or Egyptians, Greeks, and Romans) had a *notation* equal in its manipulative qualities to ours. They had *a* notation of course, but the notational development which culminated in our present system is a much later one and will be described in the next chapter. Even as late as 1514 a work on arithmetic was published in Germany in which the Hindu-Arabic numbers were explained but not used. But the concern in this chapter is only with the effort to systematize an *oral* counting process.

To appreciate the difficulty of such a development of counting by powers of ten is no easy task for the modern man. To approach the invention with some of the freshness of mind that is needed in order to pay due homage to its creators, one should first notice that it seems very evident that man created his number systems in the image of his fingers and/or toes. For in widely separated cultures anthropologists have found that the "base", as it is called, of the system is either ten, five, or twenty, with ten the most common by far. Note, too, that there is evidence of hesitation as to which choice to make in the Greek word *pempazein* (to count by fives), and such words in our own language as score and two-score. Now there is no mathematical reason to favor ten as the base, and in fact there is good reason to prefer seven, eleven, or twelve. Nevertheless the only exceptions to the five, ten, or twenty base seem to be among a few primitive tribes such as those of Australia and Africa who use a very limited form of a *binary* (base two), *ternary* (base

three) or *quaternary* (base four) system, and the Babylonians who used both base ten and base sixty.[3]

The *quinary* (base five) system rests on the same fundamental idea as the decimal system. And yet how much does
familiarity with the decimal system help in developing a
quinary system? If the reader will pause now to try to make
such a development himself, he will come away from his
labors with a heightened respect for our ancient mathematicians. For those readers not wishing to take the time, the
description of it alone will provide almost as much of an
appreciation, I am sure. Briefly, then, in the quinary system
there would be five words—say *ome, do, tee, fur,* and *fit*—to
correspond to our one, two, three, four, and five.[4] In addition there must be words for the powers of fit (as our 10^2 is
read one hundred). Suppose $(fit) \times (fit) = (fit)^2$ is called
hud. Then fit-ome would mean 5 plus 1 or our six; do fit-tee
would mean $2 \times 5 + 3$ or 13 while ome hud and do fit-tee
would mean $1 \times 5^2 + 2 \times 5 + 3$ or 38, just as our one
hundred and twenty-three means $1 \times 10^2 + 2 \times 10 + 3$ or
$100 + 20 + 3 = 123$. Now count up to hud in the quinary
system and, I hope, appreciate what the first grader is up
against!

This picture of the trials and tribulations of the six-year-
old is, I admit, somewhat overdrawn. For with training from
an early age one can easily become as proficient in counting
in the quinary or any other system as in the decimal system.
That is, one must be careful not to take an attitude similar

---

[3] Vestiges of the latter are found in our sixty seconds to one minute and
sixty minutes to one hour, as well as in the degree, minute, and second system of angle measurement.

[4] The same words could be used in the quinary system as in our decimal
system, of course, but the use of different words helps us to remember which
system we are using and will give some of the feeling of strangeness that the
child or savage has for his number words. An actual quinary system used in
the New Hebrides is as follows: *tai* (1), *lua* (2), *tolu* (3), *vari* (4), *lima*
(5—meaning hand), *o tai* (6—meaning other 1), *o lua* (7—other 2), *o tolu*
(8—other 3), *o vari* (9—other 4) and *lua lima* (10—two hands).

to that of the struggling freshman language student who
thought that French children must be awfully smart to learn
French so perfectly at such an early age! In the quinary system, in fact, we would have the advantage of having to learn
only five basic words to handle all numbers up to (our)
twenty-five, *but* the compound words for larger numbers
would be more cumbersome (compare ome hud and do fit-tee
for our thirty-eight). On the other hand, in the *vigesimal*
(base 20) system there would be more (twenty) basic names
to learn, but greater compactness in writing larger numbers.
More about this will be presented in the next chapter on the
writing of numbers in symbols. An interesting sidelight, by
the way, on the naming of numbers is the extraordinary sta-
bility of such names. The number vocabulary is so unaf-
fected by time that it is used by philologists to trace kinships
between apparently remote language groups. For example,
6 is written as *sas* in Sanskrit, *hex* in ancient Greek, *sex* in
Latin, *sechs* in German, *six* in English and French, and *shest*
in Russian.

In modern times, of course, the decimal (base ten) system is in worldwide use among civilized peoples and will undoubtedly continue to be so. But lest the complacent think,
Pangloss-like, that Divine Providence has given us ten fingers
because we get such a fine number system from it, I remark
again that the base ten, while adequate, is not ideal. For
practical purposes (i.e., computation) it would have been
better if we had been endowed with twelve fingers so that
the base twelve might have been chosen (giving rise to what
is called the *duodecimal system*). Or, on the other hand, for
theoretical reasons (the investigations of mathematicians
into the deeper secrets of numbers), a prime [5] number such
as seven or eleven would have been a better choice. Finally,

---

[5] A prime number is a number greater than one whose only divisors are
itself and one. The first ten primes are 2, 3, 5, 7, 11, 13, 17, 19, 23, and 29.

our present-day electronic computing machines (such as *Eniac*) feed best on a diet of binary numbers (e.g., 1101 in the binary system means $1 \times 2^3 + 1 \times 2^2 + 0 \times 2 + 1 \times 1 = 8 + 4 + 0 + 1 = 13$ in the decimal system) for the simple reason that an electron tube can signify "1" when it is on and "0" when it is off. Such a development would have delighted Leibnitz (cofounder with Newton of the calculus). He saw in his mathematical pet, binary arithmetic, the image of Creation where Unity represented God and Zero the Void. This naïve idea he communicated to the Jesuit, Francesco Grimaldi, president of the Chinese tribunal for mathematics, in the hope that it could be used to convert the emperor of China (who was very fond of the sciences)!

So far, history reveals no personalities to credit with specific advances. The most primitive beginnings may well have been developed and then lost again as our various early predecessors became extinct. That there was certainly no *one* development of a number system even in comparatively recent times (say the last five thousand years) is evidenced by the existence of a highly developed vigesimal system by the Mayas of Yucatan [6] at the same time that the decimal system was in use in Europe.

It is not too farfetched, however, to suppose that certain individuals did contribute more to the development of a number sense, finger counting, and the idea of a base than did others; and these men must be recognized as outstanding mathematicians comparable to the best of our time, even though today we use the principles they developed without even being conscious of them. In fact, much too frequently, teachers of elementary arithmetic have given no thought to the rhythmic procession of number names, and as a consequence many children learn to count large collections of

---

[6] Not a "pure" vigesimal system. A curious feature is their use of eighteen along with twenty.

objects by rote rather than by understanding. In a provocative but little known book,[7] Mary Boole, wife of the great nineteenth-century English mathematician George Boole, suggests that the child be taught to count ten-one, ten-two, . . . instead of eleven, twelve, ... (Note that earlier languages frequently permitted him to do just this.) Later on, she states, the child can pick up the common names for these numbers with no effort, while the possible loss of understanding which may result from the immediate use of eleven, twelve, etc. may be a long time in remedying. Although I do not know of any advocates of this procedure among contemporary educators, it is true that they are keenly aware of this point and that they warn the elementary school teacher not to treat this difficulty lightly.

PROBLEM

Count up to hud in the quinary system.

---

[7] *The Preparation of the Child for Science.* Oxford: Clarendon Press, 1904.

Chapter 2

WRITING NUMBERS FROM ONE
TO A GOOGOL

I T may seem now—as the last details of our oral counting process are completed—that nothing stands in the way of developing a corresponding notation for the *writing* of all numbers. To make an execrable pun, it is exactly nothing,[1] or the concept of a symbol for the absence of a digit, which stands in the way. For example, if we have the number one hundred and thirty-two to write in symbols, and if the symbols 1, 2, $\cdots$, 9 have been developed for the words one, two, $\cdots$, nine, we find it not too difficult an idea to put a mark, 1, for the one hundred, a 3 for the thirty, and a 2 for the two. Thus one hundred and thirty-two is written as 132, where 132 is a shorthand expression for $1 \times 100 + 3 \times 10 + 2$.

By "not too difficult" I do not mean that it is an invention that any six-year-old is capable of concocting in his spare time,[2] but rather something that a first-rate student of the Babylonian Mathematical Institute could have turned out as his thesis for the doctorate. But even he might have announced in a footnote that the problem of representing such numbers as "one hundred and two" is left for further investigation, and, for a long time, it is listed as one of the great unsolved problems of mathematics. For without the use of the symbol, 0, one hundred and two would tend to be written

---

[1] Bell says that E. H. Moore (see Chapter 10), exasperated by some of his pupils from Canada who used the word "nothing" for "zero", called "nothing" "the Canadian zero".

[2] Although, of course, he may be capable of *using* the invention.

as 12 which is immediately confused with one ten and two, or twelve.[3] How hard it is not to be impatient with the dunderheads who could not see the reasonableness of using a symbol to indicate the *absence* of a digit and hence immensely delayed the development of the number concept and, in consequence, the entire development of mathematics! So we might also rail at the stupidity of those who refused to invent the first wheel and the first boat.

Important as was the invention of the absence symbol (or zero, as we call it today), it must be admitted that a great deal of mathematics can be done without a convenient notation such as that which we enjoy. In the first place, the use of the abacus and fingers enabled people to avoid the clumsier notations of earlier times. In the second place,' computations *can* be performed directly in such notations as the Romans used, *but* they are intricate operations and are not to be entrusted to the child of eight as operations with the Hindu-Arabic numbers can be. Finally, even without the aid of a good notation for the writing of numbers, many important problems of mathematics can be solved. It is, in fact, the *applications* of mathematics rather than the mathematics itself which demand a convenient notation. The fact remains, however, that a good numeral notation is vitally necessary to reduce long operations involving large numbers, square roots, etc. to routine processes that any person of average intelligence can master. Furthermore, it seems evident that the development of mathematics as a whole would have been retarded had such a notation not been invented. And mathematics, in turn, is widely recognized as the keystone of the sciences.[4]

---

[3] Such ambiguity did exist in the early Babylonian tables, the exact value of the entry being determined by the context.

[4] In fact, Oswald Spengler in his *Decline of the West* develops the thesis that the character of each great culture is epitomized by its mathematics as much as by its art.

There are two stages in the development of our present notation for writing numbers. The first is the invention of the *principle of position* (ascribed to the Babylonians) whereby a symbol, say 2, may have different meanings according to its position in a sequence of symbols. Thus, in the sequence 52, 2 stands for two *units* (52 = five tens and two units), while in the sequence 25, 2 stands for two *tens* (25 = two tens and five units). A curious historical twist mars our story of constant advancement here in that the Babylonians as early as 1600 B.C. used this principle of position, but it was not used in other cultures until about A.D. 300! One explanation of this historical anomaly may lie in the fact that the Babylonians used two systems with different bases. (See Chapter 1.) One was the decimal system and the other the *sexigesimal* system in which the base is sixty (e.g., 21 would denote 2 × 60 + 1, or 121 in the decimal system). The decimal system was probably used mainly in connection with computations performed with the abacus, and hence few records were made in this system. But in astronomical tables and in tables of weights and measures the sexigesimal system was used, and in tables the principle of position is very important for conciseness of notation. Although the work of the Babylonians was familiar to some later cultures, they, using the decimal system exclusively, missed for centuries the "obvious" application of this principle to the decimal system.

Twenty-one Written in Some Notations Not Employing
the Principle of Position

The principle of position, however, is not sufficient in itself. There must still be invented a method of denoting the *absence* of units, tens, etc. This is the second stage in the development of the present notation for writing numbers. For example, it was pointed out that the principle of position is not sufficient to write one hundred and two in symbols without indicating in some way the absence of tens. So far as is known, no such absence symbol was used by the Babylonians until about 400 B.C. Before that time, as mentioned above, the context often had to be used to determine whether or not, for example, 21 stood for $2 \times 60 + 1$ or $2 \times 60^2 + 1$, etc.

After these two stages in the development of a written notation had been attained, computations in any system (decimal, quinary, etc.) could then be performed as we do them today, *provided* that "0" is recognized not just as an absence symbol but also as an addition to the system of whole numbers for which the basic rules of computation are given by $0 + a = a + 0 = a$, $0 \times a = a \times 0 = 0$ for every whole number a and $0 + 0 = 0 \times 0 = 0$. Such a recognition of "0" as more than just a "Canadian zero" did not immediately follow its use as an absence symbol by any means. In fact it is in another culture, that of the Hindus, that historians note the first use of the zero (around A.D. 700) as a computation symbol as well as an absence symbol.

At this point it might be well for the reader to experiment a bit with writing and computing with numbers in the quinary scale in order to appreciate better the nonobvious character of the corresponding, but familiar, work in the decimal system. For example, suppose that a, b, c, and d are the respective symbols for the word numbers ome, do, tee, and fur of the quinary system discussed in the previous chapter. In addition to these symbols, there must be an absence symbol,[5] say p, so that fit would be written as ap just as we write ten as 10 in our decimal notation. Then ac would mean $1 \times 5 + 3$ or 8 (as 13, in the decimal notation, means

---

[5] I do not choose to use 1, 2, 3, 4, and 0 for the reasons given in Chapter 1 concerning the use of ome, do, tee, fur, and fit in place of one, two, three, four, and five.

$1 \times 10 + 3$); *bad* would mean $2 \times 5^2 + 1 \times 5 + 4$ or 59 (as 214 means $2 \times 10^2 + 1 \times 10 + 4$ in the decimal notation); while *cpa* would mean $3 \times 5^2 + 0 \times 5 + 1$ or 76 (as 301 in the decimal notation means $3 \times 10^2 + 0 \times 10 + 1$). Conversely, 29 ($= 2 \times 10 + 9$) in the decimal system would be written as $1 \times 5^2 + 0 \times 5 + 4$ or *apd* and 98 ($= 9 \times 10 + 8$) as $3 \times 5^2 + 4 \times 5 + 3$ or *cdc*. To compute easily in the quinary system without going through the steps of changing from the quinary system to the decimal, we must first have addition and multiplication tables in the quinary system as shown below. (And of course school children in a quinary culture would have to memorize them!) To check a few items in the table,[6] note that $b + d$ ($2 + 4 = 6 = 1 \times 5 + 1$)

+	p	a	b	c	d
p	p	a	b	c	d
a	a	b	c	d	ap
b	b	c	d	ap	aa
c	c	d	ap	aa	ab
d	d	ap	aa	ab	ac

×	p	a	b	c	d
p	p	p	p	p	p
a	p	a	b	c	d
b	p	b	d	aa	ac
c	p	c	aa	ad	bb
d	p	d	ac	bb	ca

$= aa$; $d + c$ ($4 + 3 = 7 = 1 \times 5 + 2$) $= ab$; $b \times c$ ($2 \times 3 = 6 = 1 \times 5 + 1$) $= aa$; $c \times d$ ($3 \times 4 = 12 = 2 \times 5 + 2$) $= bb$. Of course the inventor of the original table did not have the advantage of this transformation of each part of the table into a rote-memory problem in the decimal system, so that the construction of the first such table in any system was no mean feat—and probably involved a good deal of finger counting!

---

[6] Tables like this will be met with several times. They are used as follows: To find the sum of *b* and *c*, for example, locate *b* at the extreme left-hand vertical column and *c* at the top horizontal column. The sum of *b* and *c*, *ap*, is read at the intersection of the horizontal column in which *b* lies and the vertical column in which *c* lies.

Computations then proceed in the quinary system as they do in the decimal system. This is illustrated below by working out the multiplication of *bad* by *cb*, paralleled by the equivalent operation in the decimal system (*bad* $= 2 \times 5^2 + 1 \times 5 + 4 = 59$; *cb* $= 3 \times 5 + 2 = 17$).

bad	59
cb	17
dcc	413
abpb	59
acppc	1003

Running over the steps (using the newly devised addition and multiplication tables), we have: (1) *b* times *d* is *ac*. (2) Put down *c* and carry *a*. (3) *b* times *a* is *b*, to which is added the *a* which was carried to get *c*, with nothing to carry. (4) Then *b* times *b* is *d*. (5) Now multiplying through by *c*, we have *c* times *d* is *bb*; so put down *b* and carry *b*. (6) *c* times *a* is *c*, to which is added the *b* which was carried to get *ap*. (7) So put down the *p* and carry the *a* to add to *c* times *b* ($= aa$) to get *ab*. (8) Thus we put down *ab* and now proceed to add from right to left. (9) First bring down the *c* and then have *c* + *b* is *ap* so that we put down the *p* and carry *a* to add to *d* + *p* ($= d$) to obtain *ap*. Putting down the *p*, carry the *a* to add to the *b* to get *c*, and (11), finally, bring down the last *a*. The answer, *acppc*, becomes in the decimal notation $1 \times 5^4 + 3 \times 5^3 + 0 \times 5^2 + 0 \times 5 + 3 = 625 + 375 + 0 + 0 + 3 = 1003$.

Now even if the reader has found this description of the multiplication procedure so discouragingly formidable that he has skipped most of it, the real point of the example is still gained if he realizes that *to a person accustomed to the quinary system, a similar description of the multiplication of* 59 *by* 17 *in the decimal system would look equally difficult.* And we again can appreciate the difficulties of grammar-school arithmetic when we realize that the child does not have any analogies to draw on when he meets multiplication of this type for the first time (although, of course, he *is* familiar with the symbols and the addition and multiplication tables in his system).

To recapitulate. If we consider only the period of recorded history, we see that it has taken the human race about four thousand years to perfect the speaking of, and computing with, whole numbers alone—a process which is compressed for the modern child into a scant eight or nine years. The main items I have written about have been the ideas underlying

1. A cardinal number (very early prehistoric times). Without the benefit of counting, the average person can grasp "oneness", "twoness", "threeness", and "fourness", but he cannot grasp the size of larger collections except by matching or by the use of
2. Ordinal numbers (same date as for cardinal numbers so far as is known)—the process of counting which in turn leads to the idea of
3. A word (such as "two") which applies equally well in describing the size of a collection of men as of a collection of shells (no specific date—varies from one culture to the other). And, as a final modern sophistication, we passed to
4. The concept of an abstract number not applied to any particular collection or measurement (modern times).

Then we considered

5. The systematic naming of numbers (not later than 5000 B.C. and probably earlier). At this point experimentation with number naming in the quinary system was recommended to get some small measure of appreciation of the difficulty of the task accomplished by the ancient mathematicians.

Counting out numbers in a convenient and universal fashion does not imply a similarily advantageous system for writing them (some incomplete systems were used as early as 3100 B.C.). For the writing of numbers there is needed

6. A place principle (*c.* 1600 B.C.), together with its attendant
7. Symbol for the absence of a digit (*c.* 400 B.C.) and, finally, for easy computation,
8. The recognition of zero as a number with which computations may be made (*c.* A.D. 700).

While individual names are still lacking from the story, we have, by now, passed out of the shadows which shroud the development of the number concept and the subsequent naming of numbers. The most primitive beginnings of written number do date back to prehistoric times in the form of scratches on stones, and marks on clay for numeration are at least as old as written language and probably older. The first records indicating a fairly *systematic* use of numerals, however, are those of the ancient Sumerians and Egyptians dating back to 2000 B.C. All of these early records show very similar trends in using collections of strokes for each numeral up to nine. Beyond nine, tens, hundreds, etc. are each represented by special symbols.

The stabilization of symbols for numbers has been a slow process. The first drawing below shows the present-day symbols for one, two, . . ., nine, and zero in other cultures, while the second drawing shows the slow evolution, in Western Europe, of the Hindu-Arabic numerals to their present form.

Symbols for One, . . ., Nine, and Zero in Other Cultures. (From Smith and Karpinski, *The Hindu-Arabic Numbers*, by permission of Ginn & Co.)

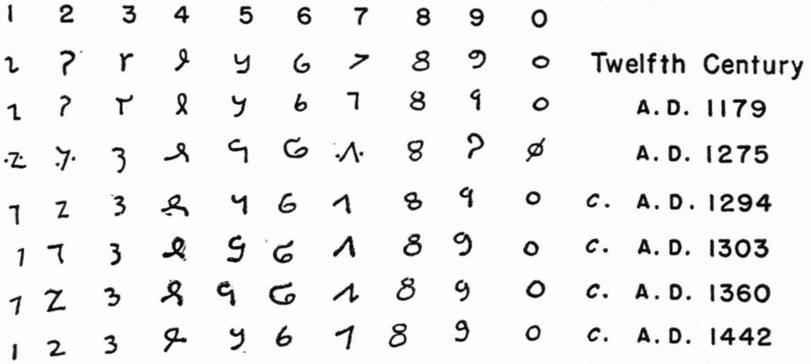

1	2	3	4	5	6	7	8	9	0	
ι	?	r	ﻻ	ﻻ	6	﹥	8	ɔ	o	Twelfth Century
ı	?	ɼ	ɣ	ﻻ	6	٦	8	٩	o	A. D. 1179
·ᴢ	·ᴦ·	3	ᴧ	٩	ﻟ	·Λ·	8	?	ø	A. D. 1275
٦	ᴢ	3	ﻼ	ᴎ	6	ᴧ	�8	٩	o	c. A. D. 1294
٦	ᴦ	3	ﻼ	9	6	Λ	8	၅	o	c. A. D. 1303
٦	ᴢ	3	ﻼ	٩	6	ᴧ	8	9	o	c. A. D. 1360
ı	ᴢ	3	ᴎ	ﻻ	6	٦	8	9	o	c. A. D. 1442

Evolution of the Hindu-Arabic Numbers. (From Smith and Karpinski, *The Hindu-Arabic Numbers*, by permission of Ginn & Co.)

To illustrate the fact that it was not only medieval man who took a long time to take advantage of better number notation, consider the remarks that Charles Dickens made in an address on Administrative Reform which he delivered a few years following the incident described below:

Ages ago a savage method of keeping accounts on notched sticks was introduced into the Court of Exchequer and the accounts were kept much as Robinson Crusoe kept his calendar on the desert island. A multitude of accountants, bookkeepers and actuaries were born and died . . .   Still official routine inclined to those notched sticks as if they were pillars of the Constitution, and still the Exchequer accounts continued to be kept on certain splints of elm-wood called "tallies." In the reign of George III an inquiry was made by some revolutionary spirit whether, pens, ink and paper, slates and pencils being in existence, this obstinate adherence to an obsolete custom ought to be continued, and whether a change ought not to be effected. All the red tape in the country grew redder at the bare mention of this bold and original conception, and it took until 1826 to get these sticks abolished. In 1834 it was found that there was a considerable accumulation of them; and the question then arose, what was to be done with such worn-out, worm-eaten, rotten old bits of wood? The sticks were housed in Westminster, and it would naturally occur to any intelligent person that nothing would be easier than to allow them to be carried away for firewood by the miserable people who lived in that neighborhood. However, they never had been useful, and official routine required that they should never be, and so the order went out that they were to be privately and confidentially burned. It came to pass that they were burned in a stove in the House of Lords. The stove, over-gorged with these preposterous sticks, set fire to the paneling; the paneling set fire to the House of Commons; the two houses were re-duced to ashes; architects were called on to build others; and we are now in the second million of the cost thereof.

One more comment before going on to more abstract mat-ters. I have suggested that it required a high order of mathe-matical ability to invent systems of notation, to develop schemes for multiplication, etc. However, the ability to in-vent does not necessarily imply that a high proficiency in the mechanical use of such artifices exists; and nothing will irk a mathematician more than to be passed the bridge score to add because he is a mathematician! As C. J. Keyser ex-pressed it: "Mathematics is no more the art of reckoning and computation than architecture is the art of making bricks or hewing wood, no more than painting is the art of mixing col-ors on a palette, no more than the science of geology is the art of breaking rocks, or the science of anatomy the art of butchering."

PROBLEMS

1. Represent 12 in the quinary system.
2. Represent 12 in the binary system.
3. Represent *apc* (quinary system) in the decimal system.
4. Represent 10101 (binary system) in the decimal system.
5. Add *apc* and *bd* in the quinary system and check by ref-erence to the decimal system.

Chapter 3

GOD MADE THE INTEGERS[1]

THE EMPHASIS on a historical approach up to this point in the book has had a twofold purpose. The first is to satisfy the interest that all of us have in origins. The question, "How did he ever think of that?" is always intriguing. The second purpose is to prepare the reader for the abstractions of modern mathematics by pointing out that even the most "obvious" ideas of today were the major inventions and abstractions of yesterday. In this chapter, however, the historical approach will be put aside temporarily in order to view the commonplace whole numbers in the abstract way that contemporary mathematicians do.

In a sense, this chapter will begin our study of *abstract* mathematics, whereas in the preceding chapters we have been studying *applied* mathematics because our thoughts centered there around the counting of material objects. By stopping now and thinking of our positive whole numbers (or positive integers) as abstractions, we shall better prepare ourselves for the more involved abstractions of later chapters.

The problem, then, is to describe, without direct reference to the process of counting material objects, a set of entities called *positive integers* which have the properties that the actual "counting" integers (whole numbers) have. Why should such an attempt be made? For essentially two reasons: the first (in which, I hope, most of my readers will join) is the desire to enjoy a fascinating and stimulating

---

[1] ". . . all else is the work of man." Leopold Kronecker (1823–1891).

game—much more interesting and far-reaching in its consequences than most games. The second is the relationship that may exist between abstract models and sets of real objects. If it should be found that the real objects possess in some sense the attributes of the model, it will follow that the properties of the model are also the properties of the real objects.

Although mathematical examples of this situation will be given later on, it may be worth while now to consider a rough analogy of this type of analysis from another field. In genetics, Mendel, working with peas, found a number of interesting laws of inheritance and in effect produced a sort of arithmetic of colors (and heights as well). So long as these principles were thought of as applying to only one type of plant, they were obviously of minor importance. But when a theoretical analysis of the general laws of combination was made, additional theoretical results were obtained which were later found to be of practical value in the cultivation of certain needed types of plants, such as hybrid corn. In other words, the scientist passes from a *special* theory, which by its very specialization may hide its own inner nature, to a *general* theory of which the original situation is a special case. The general theory is then exhaustively developed, and finally many other situations besides the original one are found to be special cases of the general one.

Thus having paid due homage in the first two chapters to the ingenious overcoming of the difficulties of notation, etc. which contributed so much to the development of our civilization, let us turn our back on all this and consider a set of objects called positive integers and denoted by the letters $a, b, c, \cdots$ with no worry about how they are named or how they are written (quinary, decimal bases; Roman, Hindu-Arabic notation, etc.). For whatever statements can be made concerning these abstract symbols will be true under all systems of notation. Furthermore (and this is an important point) mathematicians do *not* seek to *define* these positive integers since they realize that any subject has at its core a set of undefined words. That is, while the words "positive integer" may certainly be defined, any such definition would either bring in concrete objects again (which is what we are trying to avoid) or bring in other abstract terms which in turn would suggest definition. Hence it seems best to take the words "positive integer" as an undefined term, just as in elementary geometry the words "point" and "line" are undefined terms. (The futile attempt to define a point as "something which has position but not magnitude" only exchanges two "hard" words for one "easy" one!)

Even in the natural sciences a similar situation prevails. In genetics the word *gene* may be thought of as the basic undefined term, and in physics, the *proton,* the *electron,* and the *neutron* [2] (plus an increasing number of others). Now what can one gain by contemplating undefined objects? Nothing except astigmatism unless one asks what may be done with them. Thus, although at the present date most physicists are not concerned with what electrons, protons, and neutrons may be, they are greatly concerned with how they combine; for a knowledge of how they combine, without knowing just what they are, enabled these scientists to develop the atomic bomb. Parenthetically, I remark here that many of the laws of combination in both genetics and nuclear physics require for their mathematical expression the use of the more sophisticated types of numbers that will be discussed later.

---

[2] Of course these undefined objects may, in the future, be defined in terms of other quantities. Thus the atom was once considered as a single fundamental entity but is thought of today as composed of electrons, protons, and neutrons. To a limited extent the mathematician also changes his set of undefined terms for certain purposes. See, for example, the Appendix, where the (here) unspecified operations of addition and multiplication are defined in terms of the "successor" operation.

Likewise, the mathematician is interested in assuming certain properties of these positive integers in action. Action, in this sense, is the combination of positive integers by means of two operations called addition and multiplication. This concept of an *operation* is a fundamental one in mathematics and stems from the more general idea of a *function*. Since our concern here is only with a special type of operation, called a *binary* operation, let us briefly consider this concept.

The formal definition is this: A binary operation on a set S of elements *a, b, c,* ⋯ is a *rule* which assigns to each pair of elements *a* and *b* of S a uniquely defined element *c* in the same set S.[3]

EXAMPLE 1: Let S be the set of all whole numbers. Then the rule which assigns to each pair of whole numbers, *a* and *b*, their sum, $a + b \,(= c)$, is the binary operation of addition. For example, to the pair $2 \,(= a)$ and $5 \,(= b)$ is assigned $7 \,(= c)$ since $2 + 5 = 7$.

EXAMPLE 2: With S as above, the rule which assigns to each pair of whole numbers, *a* and *b*, their product, $a \times b \,(= c)$, is the binary operation of multiplication. For example, to the pair $2 \,(= a)$ and $5 \,(= b)$ is assigned $10 \,(= c)$ since $2 \times 5 = 10$.

EXAMPLE 3: With S as above, the rule which assigns to each pair of whole numbers, *a* and *b*, the remainder obtained by dividing their sum by 3 is called the binary operation of addition *modulo*[4] 3. For example, to the pair $2 \,(= a)$ and

---

[3] In common language and in elementary mathematics, an operation is considered as an act rather than a rule for performing an act. Some of the troubles that a student has in advanced mathematics stem from the frequent use of common words (such as operation, ring, ideal, open, closed) in uncommon ways.

[4] An abbreviation for the term "for the modulus". The word *modulus,* which is derived from the Latin, means "little measure".

$5 (= b)$ is assigned $1 (= c)$ since $2 + 5 = 7$ and 7 has the remainder of 1 when divided by 3.

EXAMPLE 4: Let S be the set of all the points in a plane. Then the rule which assigns to each pair of points in the plane the midpoint of line segment joining them (or, if the two points of the pair are the same, assigns the point itself) is a binary operation on this S.

EXAMPLE 5: Let S be the set of all whole numbers. Then the rule which assigns to each pair of whole numbers, a and b, their quotient, a/b, is *not* a binary operation on S. For if $a = 1$, $b = 4$, $a/b = \frac{1}{4}$ which is not a whole number (i.e., not in S) as required. If S is the set of fractions, then we do have a binary operation. Note here that it makes a difference as to which number is given first, since, for example, $\frac{1}{4}$ is not the same as $\frac{4}{1}$.

EXAMPLE 6: Let S be the set of whole numbers again. Then the rule which assigns to each number, a, its "successor", $a + 1$, is *not a binary* operation but a *unary* operation or a function.

Let us return now to our set of abstract positive integers which we were about to endow with two binary operations. Although we will call these operations addition and multiplication, we must be careful not to let our knowledge of grammar-school arithmetic lead us to suppose that we know anything in advance of the properties of the addition and multiplication of the abstract positive integers. That is, these operations on the positive integers are unspecified at present, and we must impose various conditions on them in order to construct an abstract picture of the whole numbers.

Restating our desire to have two binary operations on our set of positive integers, we have

ASSUMPTION [5] 1: For every pair of positive integers, a and b, there is assigned a unique positive integer, s, called the *sum* of a and b. We write $s = a + b$.

ASSUMPTION 2: For every pair of positive integers, a and b, there is assigned a unique positive integer, p, called the product of a and b. We write $p = a \times b$.

If the words "positive integers" are taken to mean "counting" whole numbers, Assumption 1 is certainly true. That is, a whole number plus a whole number is a whole number. Also, if the words "positive integers" are taken to mean colors and "plus" to mean the mixing of two colors (say by colored spotlights), a color is again obtained. But on the other hand, if the words "positive integers" are taken to mean gases at 70° Fahrenheit and "plus" to mean their chemical combination, Assumption 1 *may* be violated, since the "sum" of the gas hydrogen and the gas oxygen is then not a gas but a liquid. Once again; the mathematician considers an unspecified way of combining undefined objects and finds that there are certain objects in nature and certain ways of combining them for which Assumption 1 is satisfied, and other ways for which Assumption 1 is not satisfied. (Similar remarks could, of course, be made about Assumption 2.)

Now those who object to these bizarre examples of positive integers and sums might well ponder over the immortal words of Humpty Dumpty, who said (rather scornfully), "When *I* use a word, it means just what I choose it to mean —neither more nor less." And if the reader, like Alice, protests: "The question is whether you *can* make words mean so many different things," we may again quote Mr. Dumpty,

---

[5] Also called an "axiom"—a term today used synonomously with "assumption" by mathematicians. At one time, however, an axiom was considered as a "self-evident truth" (whatever that is!), and it is still used in this sense by some elementary geometry books. Hence the word "assumption" is preferable here to avoid such false connotations.

who replied to Alice, "The question is which is to be master —that's all."

These assumptions are still too meager to derive the consequences we wish for; so the mathematician hastens to add several others. In each of the statements below it is to be understood that the rule holds for *all* positive integers, *a*, *b*, and *c*.

ASSUMPTION 3: $a + b = b + a$, the commutative law for addition.

ASSUMPTION 4: $a \times b = b \times a$, the commutative law for multiplication.

ASSUMPTION 5: $(a + b) + c = a + (b + c)$, the associative law for addition.

ASSUMPTION 6: $(a \times b) \times c = a \times (b \times c)$, the associative law for multiplication.

ASSUMPTION 7: $a \times (b + c) = a \times b + a \times c$, the distributive law for addition with respect to multiplication.

In discussing these assumptions in turn, I shall first illustrate that each one is a valid one for the whole numbers; then I shall show the existence of other objects, together with suitable meanings for addition and multiplication,[6] which also satisfy the assumption under discussion. And, finally, I shall show the existence of sets for which the assumption is false. Notice that in each example it must not only be stated what the objects considered as positive integers are but also what is meant by addition and/or multiplication.

ASSUMPTION 3: $a + b = b + a$, the commutative law for addition.

---

[6] Equality is sometimes taken to be one of the basic concepts of logic not subject to further definition or mathematical analysis. However, it is often desirable to subject it to a discussion and to demand that equality satisfy certain conditions that are discussed in the Appendix. In the strictly mathematical material discussed in the examples, it will suffice to regard equality as logical identity while, it must be confessed, the idea of equality is used somewhat loosely in the nonmathematical examples.

(1) Here the set under consideration is the set of whole numbers for which Assumptions 1 and 2 certainly hold. Now, for example, $2 + 3 = 5$ means that the counting of the set of squares in Figure 1, followed by the counting of the set of

<table>
<tr><td>Figure 1</td><td>Figure 2</td></tr>
</table>

squares in Figure 2, yields 5, and likewise $3 + 2 = 5$ means that the counting of the set of squares in Figure 2 followed by the counting of the set of squares in Figure 1 also yields 5. That is, $2 + 3 = 3 + 2$. It should be noted that while every educated adult regards $2 + 3 = 3 + 2$ as obvious, educators have shown that the child learning to add may readily give the answer to $2 + 3$ and then hesitate over $3 + 2$.

(2) Here our set of integers consists of all line segments in a plane drawn from a fixed point O on the plane. In particular, let a be a line segment drawn from the point O. Physically, it may be taken to represent a pull on an object at O. For example, if a pull of one pound exerted in a northeasterly direction is applied at O, draw a line, a, of length one inch in that direction. Similarly, line b, two inches long, represents a pull of two pounds at O in an easterly direction.

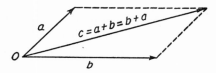

Line c, the diagonal of the parallelogram which has lines a and b as sides, represents the magnitude of the "resultant" pull at O, and if the object at O is movable, it will move along the line c. That is, the effect of the single force represented by c is the same as the effect of the two forces represented by a and b. Such "directed lines" are called *vectors*, and the vector c is said to be the sum of the vectors a and b.

We write $c = a + b = b + a$. Note that Assumption 1 is satisfied.

(3a) (This one is for men only!) Here the set under consideration is the set of all acts performed on one's face! In particular, let a be the act of lathering your face and b be the act of gliding a razor over it. $a + b$ is the act of performing these functions in that order (remember that $+$ may be specified as any operation subject only to the restrictions of Assumption 1). Clearly, $a + b$ is not equal to $b + a$ in the sense of equality as a sensation. Here, in order to have Assumption 1 hold, we must consider the sum of two acts as itself an act (as the act of shaving in the example). We will not try to define a multiplication of these terms! Actually, this bizarre example is not to be taken too seriously. The difficulty of obtaining a more reasonable and mathematical example is that the additive process is assumed commutative in all present mathematical investigations.[7]

(3b) (This one is for women only!) Here the set under consideration is the set of all acts performed on a floor! Specifically, let a be the act of washing the floor and b be the act of waxing it. If $a + b$ means the act of performing these functions in that order, it is clear that $a + b$ is not equal to $b + a$ in the sense of equality as the same in appearance. (See, also, the comments on Example 3a.)

ASSUMPTION 4: $a \times b = b \times a$, the commutative law for multiplication.

(1) With the set under consideration taken to be the set of whole numbers, 2×3 represents two sets of three each, or six, while 3×2 represents three sets of two each—still six.

(2) Here we take as an element of our set any set of points in a plane. In particular, let a be the set of all the

---

[7] In noncommutative *groups*, the group operation may be thought of as either an addition or a multiplication. It is customary, however, to reserve the addition symbol for commutative groups.

points in circle *a*, and *b* the set of all the points in circle *b*.
By *a* × *b* is meant all the points in circle *a* which are also in
circle *b*, while by *b* × *a* is meant all the points in circle *b*
which are also in circle *a*. Clearly, the same points are de-

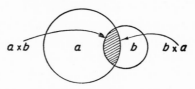

scribed by the symbol *b* × *a* as by *a* × *b* and *a* × *b* = *b* × *a*
in that sense. These point sets are of the utmost importance
in the development of a complete theory of the calculus.
They have also recently been used as a basic tool by John
von Neumann and Oskar Morgenstern in their *Theory of
Games and Economic Behavior* [8]—a work about which a
reviewer wrote, "Posterity may regard this book as one of
the major scientific achievements of the first half of the
twentieth century."

(3) We now take our set to be all vectors originating
from a point in any direction and not just in a plane. Addition of vectors was defined in the second example under the
discussion of the commutative law of addition. It is also
possible to define a multiplication [9] of vectors which is a noncommutative operation. What the physicist does is to say
that *a* × *b* is a vector perpendicular to the plane of the paper

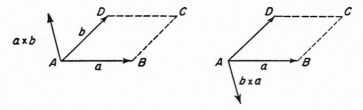

[8] Princeton University Press, 1947.

[9] Actually, two kinds of products are used. The "dot" product is a commutative operation in contrast to the "cross" product discussed here.

on which *a* and *b* are drawn, with length numerically equal to the area of the parallelogram *ABCD, and which is directed upward.* On the other hand, $b \times a$ has the same length as $a \times b$, *but is directed downward.* Such a product vector, for example, can be used to obtain the force developed by the action of the magnetic field on the current-carrying conductors of an electric motor. In such a case it is clearly important to know not only the magnitude of the force but also in what direction it is exerted; otherwise we shall not know whether the motor will turn in a clockwise or in a counterclockwise direction.

ASSUMPTION 5: $a + (b + c) = (a + b) + c$, the associative law for addition.

(1) If our set is the set of whole numbers, we have, for example, $(2 + 3) + 4 = 5 + 4 = 9$ while $2 + (3 + 4) = 2 + 7 = 9$.

(2) If our set is the set of all vectors in a plane originating from a point *O*, see the figure below for the addition of three vectors according to the rules laid down in the discussion of the commutative law for addition. Again, $a + (b + c) = (a + b) + c$.

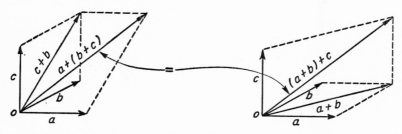

(3) Now take our set to be the set of ordinary positive fractions (including whole numbers). Since the operation of addition is unspecified, we may ask whether it would be permissible to take it as the operation of division. That is, for *a* and *b* fractions, may we take $a + b$ to mean *a* divided by *b*?

If this query seems altogether ridiculous to the reader, it is only because he is continuing to think that the operation which is called addition is actually one that he knows all about—rather than an unspecified operation. In any case, if we accept $a + b$ to mean a divided by b, Assumption 5 is violated. For (60 divided by 6) divided by 2, is 10 divided by 2, or 5, while 60 divided by (6 divided by 2) is 60 divided by 3, or 20. Again, the triviality of the example is due to the fact that, to date, addition in mathematical systems has been assumed to be associative. And the reason for including fractions as well as whole numbers in our set is that the quotient of, for example, 2 by 4 is not a whole number but the fraction $\frac{1}{2}$. Hence Assumption 1 would be violated if fractions were not included in the set. Note also that division is not, in general, a commutative operation. That is, a divided by b is not equal to b divided by a unless a is equal to b.

ASSUMPTION 6: $a \times (b \times c) = (a \times b) \times c$, the associative law for multiplication.

(1) With our set again the set of whole numbers, we have, for example, $2 \times (3 \times 4) = (2 \times 3) \times 4$, since $2 \times (3 \times 4) = 2 \times 12 = 24$ while $(2 \times 3) \times 4 = 6 \times 4 = 24$.

(2) Consider the point sets again with multiplication defined as in Example 2 under the discussion of the commuta-

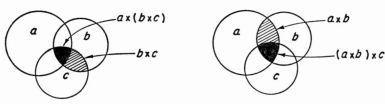

tive law for multiplication; $a \times (b \times c)$ is the set of all points in a that are also in b and c; $(a \times b) \times c$ is the set of all points in a and b that are also in c.

(3) Example 3 on the associative law for addition serves equally well here. Or the reader may prefer to wait until

Chapter 11 where some less artificial examples will be presented.

ASSUMPTION 7: $a \times (b + c) = a \times b + a \times c$, the distributive law.

(1) With, once more, our set as the set of whole numbers, we have, for example, $2 \times (3 + 4) = 2 \times 7 = 14$ while $2 \times 3 + 2 \times 4 = 6 + 8 = 14$.

(2) The points in a plane again (see Example 2 under Assumption 4), where by $b + c$ is meant simply the points in the circle b, *together* with the points in the circle c.

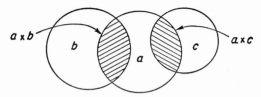

$a \times (b + c)$ is the set of all points that are in a *and* in b or c, $a \times b + a \times c$ is the set of all points that are in a *and* b *or* in a *and* c.

(3) There are many examples of mathematical systems in which addition and multiplication are defined which satisfy Assumptions 1 to 6 but not Assumption 7. Such systems, for example those called nondistributive *lattices*, are, however, too technical to describe here without digressing considerably. Recently, too, it has been shown [10] that work in the theory of errors of physical measurements involves a violation of the distributive law. But this, too, is rather technical. A simple example of the failure of Assumption 7 (and, however, Assumption 5 as well) is afforded by taking the set under consideration as the set of whole numbers and defining

$$a \oplus b = a^2 + b^2,$$

[10] L. C. Green, "Maximum Uncertainty as a Simple Example of a Nondistributive Algebra", *American Mathematical Monthly*, Vol. 55 (1948), pp. 363–64.

where the plus sign on the right stands for ordinary addition and the encircled plus on the left is our defined addition. Multiplication will be taken in the ordinary sense. Then, for example,

$$2 \times (3 \oplus 4) = 2 \times (3^2 + 4^2) = 2 \times (9 + 16) = 2 \times 25 = 50,$$

while

$$2 \times 3 \oplus 2 \times 4 = 6 \oplus 8 = 6^2 + 8^2 = 36 + 64 = 100.$$

Thus $2 \times (3 \oplus 4) \neq 2 \times 3 \oplus 2 \times 4$. (The symbol $\neq$ is read "not equal to".)

The point has now been reached where many properties of the set of positive integers under addition and multiplication may be proved. Before this is done, however, it might be well to examine a more familiar type of mathematics where this sort of thing happens. This is the high-school geometry invoked earlier in connection with the discussion of undefined entities such as points and lines. Certain properties, called postulates or axioms, are then ascribed to these points and lines, such as the famous "parallel" postulate: "Through every point not on a given line, one and only one line can be drawn parallel to the given line."

As in the case of the arithmetic student and the integers, the geometry student thinks of points and lines as concrete objects rather than abstractions and he regards the axioms and postulates as "self-evident". But, just as in the situation here, a careful study of the subject will reveal the basic abstractness; and geometries *can* be constructed which violate the "self-evident" postulates. In particular, so-called non-Euclidean geometries have been invented which violate this "parallel" postulate.[11]

---

[11] See L. R. and H. G. Lieber, *Non-Euclidean Geometry*, New York: Academy Press, 1931.

But while in geometry, systematic [12] use is made of postulates in the proofs of theorems, this pattern is not followed in the study of high-school and first-year college algebra. Instead, class time is largely devoted to drill in mechanical manipulation and in applications to word problems. This is, perhaps, a necessary way to proceed, since the manipulations and applications of algebra are so vital for work in calculus, physics, chemistry, etc. On the other hand, such a method of teaching algebra creates a false impression of the subject as it exists today in the minds of mathematicians,[13] and it certainly does not help the reader to follow the arguments of this chapter.

The theorem proved here is just a sample of the type of result that can be obtained. Its proof will be presented in the same form as a geometric proof so that the reader may possibly draw upon his recollections of that subject [14] to aid him in following the argument.

THEOREM 1: $(b + c) \times a = b \times a + c \times a.$

That is, while $a \times (b + c) = a \times b + a \times c$ is *assumed*, $(b + c) \times a = b \times a + c \times a$ may be *proved*. The first of these statements should really be called the left-hand distributive law, and the second the right-hand distributive law.

---

[12] Comparatively speaking! But as a reader of the manuscript aptly said, it is actually a mixture of "postulates, geometric intuition, and abracadabra"! And even the original Euclid is not free of logical flaws.

[13] Thus, I once heard two young freshmen discussing one of America's leading algebraists whom they, apparently, greatly admired as their teacher. One said, "Gee, he can solve quadratic equations as quick as a wink." The other, seeking to top his friend's remark, said, "Yeh, and I bet he can solve cubic equations, too." Actually this man is probably less adept at such mechanical procedure than many a high-school teacher, but he excels in the type of abstract analysis described here.

[14] He may, of course, have no recollections, or he may never have taken the subject! But the form is still the easiest to follow.

Proof:

STEPS   REASONS

1. $b + c = f$—another positive integer   Assumption 1
2. $(b + c) \times a = f \times a$ Substitution[15] of f for $b + c$
3. $f \times a = a \times f$ Assumption 4
4. $a \times f = a \times (b + c)$ Substitution of $b + c$ for f
5. $a \times (b + c) = a \times b + a \times c$ Assumption 7
6. $a \times b + a \times c = b \times a + c \times a$ Assumption 4, applied twice

Q.E.D.

The important thing to note here is that, since the term *positive integer* is undefined, this theorem holds for all objects which, together with their operations, satisfy Assumptions 1, 4, and 7. Since the point sets may be shown to satisfy these assumptions, there has been proved, at one blow, a theorem concerning whole numbers *and* point sets (as well as many other sets of mathematical objects) instead of separate proofs being required in each case. Of course the proof of this theorem could have been given earlier by changing the order of the assumptions, since only 1, 4, and 7 were used. However, I have preferred to follow the order of assumptions usually given and to discuss all the "operational" assumptions at one time. Other examples of this type of argument will be given in later chapters.

Nowadays almost every introductory graduate course in mathematics (such as real function theory, group theory, and linear algebras) begins with a recitation of a list of assumptions concerning the (undefined) objects and operations under discussion. That such a procedure is necessary in order to avoid later difficulties was only vaguely recognized just a hundred years ago, despite the work of Euclid

---

[15] Of course, we are actually making another assumption at this point—namely, that such a procedure of "substituting equals for equals" is legitimate, or else we can use the idea of logical identity. This question also bears on the meaning of equality which I avoided discussing earlier. I shall not discuss this principle here but again refer the interested reader to the Appendix.

(*c.* 300 B.C.) which set such a fine precedent over two thousand years ago. In fact, for many centuries, mathematicians regarded the postulates and axioms of Euclid (with one exception) as "self-evident" truths—i.e., statements that any person with any degree of common sense should see *had* to be true about points and lines. The one exception was the "parallel" axiom, and many attempts were made to prove it by use of the remaining "self-evident" axioms. These attempts necessarily failed, for as Nicolai Lobachevsky (1793–1856) showed in 1829, there exist geometries in which all the axioms *except* the parallel axiom hold.[16] It is not my purpose here to go afield into a description of the development of geometry, but simply to make the reader realize that the analogy to the development of algebra is very close. Furthermore, Lobachevsky in "liberating" geometry did much to influence the development of the postulational approach in other fields of mathematics.

In the early nineteenth century there developed a school of British mathematicians who began to treat algebra in the modern spirit. In his *Treatise on Algebra,* published in 1830, George Peacock (1791–1858) paid serious attention for perhaps the first time in the history of mathematics to the fundamental principles of algebra (our assumptions) and broke with the primitive tradition that, in such statements as $a + b = b + a$ and $a \times b = b \times a$, a and b necessarily represent numbers. Later, I shall speak of men who actually described systems in which a and b do represent other quantities besides ordinary numbers.

This modern point of view has been expressed (in perhaps a somewhat extreme fashion) by Bertrand Russell, who wrote:

Pure mathematics consists entirely of such asseverations as that, if such and such a proposition is true of *anything*, then such and such

---

[16] And one of these geometries, according to Einstein, is a better "image" of our universe than the Euclidean geometry!

another proposition is true of that thing. It is essential not to discuss whether the first proposition is really true, and not to mention what the anything is of which it is supposed to be true . . . Thus mathematics may be defined as the subject in which we never know what we are talking about, nor whether what we are saying is true.[17]

The extremeness is, of course, only in the last sentence. After reading what has come before this quotation, the reader should not find it too hard to take. But I object to springing this definition—as is often done—without such preparation!

PROBLEMS

1. With the usual meanings of addition and multiplication, does the set of all *odd* numbers satisfy Assumptions 1 and 2? Answer the same question for the set of even numbers.

2. If the words "positive integer" stand for a complete sentence of three words, and the sum of two sentences to mean the following combination of words: the first word of the first sentence, followed by the second word of the second sentence, and concluded by the third word of the first sentence, does Assumption 1 always hold or not?

3. If a stands for the sentence "I love Mary", and b stands for the sentence "You hate Mary", is $a + b = b + a$ if plus is defined as in Problem 2 and equality means the same emotion?

4. Verify the distributive law, $a \times (b + c) = a \times b + a \times c$, for the point sets shown below.

5. Using $a = 2$, $b = 3$, and $c = 4$, show that the associative law of addition is not satisfied when $a \oplus b = a^2 + b^2$. (See discussion of the distributive law.)

6. Prove that $a \times [b + (c + d)] = a \times b + (a \times c + a \times d)$.

---

[17] *Mysticism and Logic* (New York: W. W. Norton & Co., Inc., 1929).

Chapter 4

CREATION COMPLETED

CHAPTER 3 gives the assumptions concerning operations with positive integers which tally with the properties of the corresponding operations performed with ordinary whole numbers. The first two assumptions noted ($a + b$ and $a \times b$ are positive integers if a and b are positive integers) are what might be called "closure" assumptions. That is, it is assumed that addition and multiplication, respectively, never develop a type of quantity different from the ones with which we began. Obviously, with just two operations, no further closure assumptions are necessary. Then the five "operational-equality" assumptions were presented which are commonly called the fundamental laws of arithmetic.

For a number of situations that arise in arithmetic, however, another assumption is needed. For all the way through the development I have presented, the set of ordinary whole numbers has been thought of as a concrete "model" of the abstract positive integers; and among the throng of whole numbers, *unity* is certainly present. That is, there is a whole number, denoted by "1", with the property that $1 \times 2 = 2$, $1 \times 3 = 3$, etc. Now the assumptions listed to date say nothing about the existence of such a unit element, and in fact the set of whole numbers with the *exception* of unity satisfy all the assumptions. Hence, in order to make the abstract set more like the whole numbers, the mathematician adds

ASSUMPTION 8: There is a positive integer, denoted by "1", such that $a \times 1 = 1 \times a = a$ for every positive integer a.

In the vector situation it is easy to see that there is no such "unit" vector, for as explained in Chapter 3, $a \times b$ is a vector *perpendicular* to the plane containing the two vectors a and b, and if $a \neq 0$, certainly cannot coincide with a no matter what the vector b may be taken to be. But in the point set case, "1" is the set of all points in the plane. For the set of points common to any given set of points a and all the points in the plane is certainly the set of points a.

So far, at least, the point sets are still candidates for the title of positive integers in that they satisfy all the assumptions that have been made about the positive integers. They may now be eliminated by virtue of the second part of

ASSUMPTION 9: The cancellation laws hold:

if $a + c = b + c$, then $a = b$; if $a \times c = b \times c$, then $a = b$,

for all positive integers a, b, and c.

For while these are elementary laws of arithmetic for whole numbers, in the point set case we may have $a \times c = b \times c$ but $a \neq b$ as shown below.

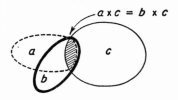

At this point, by the way, the reader may well marvel at the mathematicians' perversity that causes them to rejoice in the existence of these point sets that have properties in common with the positive integers in Chapter 3, and to exult over their elimination in the very next chapter. But in so doing they are simply alternately following two divergent lines of development, both of which are common in the mathematical work of today. Thus the mathematician is interested in studying at the same time a whole series of related mathematical sets of objects (as positive integers, point sets, vectors, etc.); but on the other hand he wants to be able to distinguish in some mathematical way between the members of this series.

In any case, when he eliminates the point sets as positive integers, it is natural to ask whether any other system besides the set of ordinary whole numbers satisfies all nine assumptions. The answer is "yes". For example, the set of all positive fractions (including whole numbers as special cases). Note that we are thinking of fractions here in the intuitive sense of grade-school arithmetic and not in the abstract sense of a later chapter. In this sense, then, we are simply saying that the laws of computation with "grade-school" fractions are the same as those for "grade-school" whole numbers. *But* the set of fractions does not possess the following basic and noncomputational property of the whole numbers which I list as Assumption 10 for the positive integers.

ASSUMPTION 10: Principle of finite induction. A set of positive integers which includes 1 and which includes $n + 1$ whenever it includes n, includes *every* positive integer.

That is, it is impossible to write down a set of positive integers which includes 1 and, whenever it includes a certain positive integer n, includes that integer's "successor", $n + 1$, without writing down all the positive integers.

Now this is clearly a property of the whole numbers. On the other hand, the set of positive fractions does not satisfy Assumption 10 and hence cannot be considered as a model of the positive integers. For example, if we consider the set of fractions

$$\frac{1}{2}, \ 1, \ 1\frac{1}{2}, \ 2, \ 2\frac{1}{2}, \ 3, \ 3\frac{1}{2}, \ 4, \ 4\frac{1}{2}, \ \cdots$$

and so on indefinitely, we have a set of quantities which includes 1 and, whenever it includes n, includes $n + 1$. That is,

1 is there, so $1 + 1 = 2$ is there; 2 is there, so $2 + 1 = 3$ is there; $\frac{1}{2}$ is there, so $\frac{1}{2} + 1 = 1\frac{1}{2}$ is there; etc. But this set of fractions certainly does not contain all possible fractions (as, for example, $\frac{3}{4}$). Hence Assumption 10 fails.

Finally, one more assumption is needed in order to make sure that "essentially" (I shall define this term later) the only set corresponding to what we are calling the positive integers is the set of ordinary whole numbers.

ASSUMPTION 11: For any two positive integers a and b, exactly *one* of the following alternatives holds: $a = b$, or there is a positive integer x such that $a + x = b$, or there is a positive integer y such that $a = b + y$.

For example, in the case of the whole numbers, if $a = 3$ and $b = 5$, we have $x = 2$ ($3 + 2 = 5$) and there is no y such that $3 = 5 + y$, while if $a = 5$ and $b = 3$ we have $y = 2$ ($5 = 3 + 2$) and there is no x such that $5 + x = 3$. I shall not discuss the reason for the necessity of this additional assumption here (see Appendix) but include it simply for the sake of completeness.

Thus, finally, we have completed a treatment of our basic entities, the positive integers, and we are ready to go on to many extensions of them. Before we do so, however, a recapitulation and a few additional remarks are in order. First of all, what we have done is to describe a set of abstract (undefined) quantities called positive integers which behave like our ordinary whole numbers by the device of postulating certain properties of these positive integers. Along the way we noted that until we reached Assumption 11 there were many candidates for the title of positive integers and that these were gradually eliminated as we imposed more qualifications for the title.

But it may now be stated that the properties described in Assumptions 1 to 11 completely characterize the positive integers as the abstract equivalents of the ordinary whole numbers in the sense that ordinary whole numbers certainly do have these properties, and that any other set satisfying these assumptions can be proved to be *isomorphic* to the set of ordinary whole numbers. This idea of "isomorphism" is a basic concept of algebra. Loosely speaking, two sets of quantities, each with two binary operations (addition and multiplication) are said to be isomorphic if they differ only in the *notation*. Thus the set of whole numbers itself may be written in many different notations as, for example, Roman or Hindu-Arabic. But the set considered in each case is still that of the whole numbers.

A simple example may help to make this concept of isomorphism clearer. We all know that the sum of two even numbers is even; the sum of two odd numbers is even and the sum of an odd number and an even number is odd. Also the product of two even numbers is even, the product of two odd numbers is odd, and the product of an odd number and an even number is even. Symbolically, we have

$$\text{even} + \text{even} = \text{even} \qquad \text{odd} + \text{even} = \text{odd}$$
$$\text{even} + \text{odd} = \text{odd} \qquad \text{odd} + \text{odd} = \text{even}$$

$$\text{even} \times \text{even} = \text{even} \qquad \text{odd} \times \text{even} = \text{even}$$
$$\text{even} \times \text{odd} = \text{even} \qquad \text{odd} \times \text{odd} = \text{odd}$$

Or, letting "even" be represented by a and "odd" be represented by b, we have

$$a + a = a \qquad b + a = b$$
$$a + b = b \qquad b + b = a$$

$$a \times a = a \qquad b \times a = a$$
$$a \times b = a \qquad b \times b = b$$

Let us call this the algebra of "even" and "odd".

On the other hand, let us consider two whole numbers "equal" if their remainders are equal (in the ordinary sense) upon division by two. That is, $0 \,"="\, 2 \,"="\, 4 \,"="\, 6 \,"="\, \cdots$ since $0, 2, 4, 6, \cdots$ all have remainders of 0 when divided

by 2. Similarly we have 1 "=" 3 "=" 5 "=" 7 "=" ⋯ since
1, 3, 5, 7, ⋯ all have remainders of 1 when divided by 2.
Then we can say (dropping the quotes on the equal signs)
that

$$0+0 = 0 \qquad 1+0 = 1$$
$$0+1 = 1 \qquad 1+1 = 0$$
$$0 \times 0 = 0 \qquad 1 \times 0 = 0$$
$$0 \times 1 = 0 \qquad 1 \times 1 = 1$$

where all the results of the computations are simply consequences of ordinary arithmetic except $1 + 1 = 0$, and this is
a consequence of our identification of 0 with 2 (since 0 and 2
have the same remainder upon division by 2). This tiny system goes under the impressive name of the algebra of integers modulo 2.

Now if we let 0 be represented by a and 1 by b, what do
we find that our 0, 1 computation table becomes? Why exactly the a, b table obtained from the even, odd table. We
thus see that the algebra of "even" and "odd" and the algebra
of integers modulo 2 differ only in the notation for their
elements and thus are isomorphic.[1]

In passing it may be of interest to note that the idea of
equality (*congruence* in technical language) "modulo 2" can
be extended to equality modulo 3, 4, 5, etc. For example,
under equality modulo 3 we have 0 "=" 3 "=" 6 "=" 9 ⋯,
1 "=" 4 "=" 7 "=" 10 ⋯, 2 "=" 5 "=" 8 "=" 11 ⋯ . A system of integers modulo 29 or 31 has recently been used in
cryptography, while the general idea of "=" or congruence is
extremely useful in the "theory of numbers" where, for example, it can be applied to such problems as determining the

---

[1] In fact they are rather transparently isomorphic, since to say that a
number has a remainder of 0 upon division by 2 is a "fancy" way of saying
that it is even. Likewise, a remainder of 1 upon division by 2 is equivalent
to the property of oddness.

day of the week on which a certain date falls or the date of Easter.[2]

In concluding this treatment of the positive integers, two important final remarks should be made. First of all it is not logically necessary to begin the study of modern algebra via the consideration of positive integers. It is simply *a* way of beginning which, I feel, is most suitable for my purposes. Second, if one does choose to begin with the positive integers, it should be emphasized that the particular eleven assumptions I have used to characterize the positive integers are not the only ones which could be used. *Some* assumptions are needed, of course, and the ones I have selected are commonly used in introductory treatments. A more sophisticated and more difficult approach which is commonly used in more advanced works is that due to G. Peano (1858–1932) of Italy. It is discussed briefly in the Appendix.

PROBLEM

Decide which of the eleven assumptions are satisfied by the algebra of "even" and "odd" (or, equivalently, the algebra of integers modulo 2).

---

[2] See, for example, J. V. Uspensky and M. A. Heaslet, *Elementary Number Theory*, McGraw-Hill Book Co., Inc., 1939, pp. 206–21.

Chapter 5

ZERO AGAIN—AND LESS

HAVING given due consideration to the fundamental building stones of the mathematical edifice we are erecting, we turn our attention to what else is needed. In this chapter, then, we shall enlarge our set of positive integers to include zero and the negative integers to obtain what is called the set of *integers*.

Zero and the negative numbers can be introduced in a purely formal fashion, as we did the positive integers in Chapter 3. This is the process usually followed in graduate work. However, it will certainly help to make the subject more understandable if I introduce these concepts in a more constructive fashion via the study of algebraic equations. This is a method which has both logical and historical sanction. It is *not* the approach, by the way, of the schools, where negative numbers are introduced by pointing out that we have temperatures below zero as well as above, debits as well as credits, etc. In other words, there the attempt is made to make negative numbers as concrete and real to the student as positive numbers. Historically, however, the use of negative numbers began before any practical applications of them were perceived! How did this happen?

Basically it was a consequence of the universal desire among mathematicians to have a rule apply without exception. That is, by studying certain algebraic equations for which positive solutions were available and then observing certain very similar appearing equations for which no positive solutions existed, the Hindu mathematicians of around A.D. 900 found it necessary to *invent* negative numbers (or integers).

Specifically, consider the series of simple equations (1) $x + 4 = 5$; (2) $x + 3 = 6$; and (3) $x + 5 = 7$. Clearly the solutions are, respectively, (1) $x = 1$, (2) $x = 3$, and (3) $x = 2$. As remarked before, mathematicians dearly love to generalize and embody special cases in one general case. Thus a mathematician would say that he was studying the solution of equations, all of the form

$$x + b = a,$$

where a and b are positive integers. *If b is less than a,* it is clear that the rule for finding x is to subtract b from a. Suppose, now, that b is *greater* than a. A desire to have the rule continue to hold in this new situation leads the mathematician to write $a - b$ as the solution anyway. Thus, for the equation

$$x + 3 = 2,$$

he has the solution, as yet purely symbolic, $x = 2 - 3$. Generalizing this idea, he considers *pairs* of positive integers, a and b, written as $a - b$, and makes the definitions:

1. $a - b = c - d$ if $a + d = b + c$.

For example, $2 - 3 = 4 - 5$ because $2 + 5 = 3 + 4$, i.e., both pairs represent the same number, -1.

2. $(a - b) + (c - d) = (a + c) - (b + d)$.

For example, $(2 - 3) + (4 - 6) = (2 + 4) - (3 + 6) = 6 - 9 = 1 - 4$, i.e., $(-1) + (-2) = (-3)$.

3. $(a - b) \times (c - d) = (a \times c + b \times d) - (a \times d + b \times c)$.

For example, $(2 - 3) \times (4 - 6) = (2 \times 4 + 3 \times 6) - (2 \times 6 + 3 \times 4) = (8 + 18) - (12 + 12) = 26 - 24$, i.e., $(-1) \times (-2) = (+2)$.

Several comments on these definitions are now in order. First of all, it is important to note that we are trying to avoid having these newly introduced symbols to be immediately identified with the ordinary signed numbers of elementary algebra. It is true, of course, that the properties of, say, the symbol $1 - 2$, are intended to duplicate the properties of its concrete counterpart, -1, but we want to consider the symbols $a - b$ just as much abstractions as we did the original symbols a and b used in Chapters 3 and 4. All that is insisted on is that it be known when two such symbols are to be identified (Definition 1) and how to add and multiply two such symbols (Definitions 2 and 3, respectively). Furthermore, it is vital to observe that the definition of equality involves only a knowledge of addition and equality for *positive* integers; the definition of addition involves only a knowledge of addition for *positive* integers; and the definition of multiplication involves only a knowledge of addition and multiplication for *positive* integers.

Secondly, it should be pointed out that it is quite customary in formal courses in advanced algebra to use the symbol (a, b) for our $a - b$, and furthermore, to continue the use of the symbol (a, b) for the other pairs of numbers which we shall use later. The advantage of the parentheses notation is that it immediately removes the temptation to identify the abstraction of, say, $(1, 2)$ with the concrete -1. On the other hand, however, I feel that the use of the parentheses notation tends to cause the beginner in the subject to lose sight of the fact that, after all, we *are* trying to construct an abstract image of the ordinary signed numbers. Furthermore, the reader may well have used the symbol (a, b) as the algebraic designation for a point in a rectangular coordinate system (as in graphing) and resent the use of the same symbol here for another purpose. It is only fair, however, to warn the reader that some of the books mentioned in the bibliography do use (a, b) for $a - b$.

Finally, whenever operations are defined on pairs of numbers where it is possible to have two seemingly different pairs equal (as $2 - 3 = 4 - 5$) it is important to consider what is called the *invariance* of the operations under the equality relation. For example, we have shown that (under Definition 2)

$$(2 - 3) + (4 - 6) = 1 - 4.$$

On the other hand, since $2 - 3 = 4 - 5$ and $4 - 6 = 5 - 7$, we must have

$$(2 - 3) + (4 - 6) = (4 - 5) + (5 - 7)$$

in order to assure uniqueness of answer to this addition problem. Now

$$(4 - 5) + (5 - 7) = (4 + 5) - (5 + 7) = 9 - 12$$

and, fortunately, $9 - 12$ is equal to $1 - 4$ since $9 + 4 = 13 = 12 + 1$ (see Definition 1).

In general, then, if $a - b = a' - b'$ and $c - d = c' - d'$ we wish to make sure that

$$(a - b) + (c - d) = (a' - b') + (c' - d')$$

and

$$(a - b) \times (c - d) = (a' - b') \times (c' - d').$$

These equations are discussed in the Appendix.[1]

To summarize. A new class of numbers, written as $a - b$ where a and b are positive integers, has been defined, and equality, addition, and multiplication have been prescribed in such a way that a knowledge of the behavior of *positive* integers alone enables us to operate with these numbers. These new numbers, of course, do behave like the negative numbers commonly used when b is greater than[2] a (as the examples show). Furthermore, there is no denying the fact that the definitions were designed with precisely that aim in

---

[1] Actually we are defining sums and products of the *class* of all pairs "equal" to $a - b$ and the *class* of all pairs "equal" to $c - d$.

[2] The reader knows what "greater than" means in the case of ordinary whole numbers. For the abstract positive integers, this concept needs to be defined. But rather than interrupt the development here, we relegate the discussion of this concept to the Appendix.

mind. But regardless of the meaning or lack of meaning of these symbols, the salient fact is that the operations have all been referred to the positive integers.

Continuing, note next that not only has a new class of numbers called integers been described, but that this new class includes, as a special case, a class of numbers isomorphic to the previously discussed positive integers. Explicitly, the isomorphism is given by

4. $(a+1)-1$ corresponds to a for every positive integer a.

That is, the positive integer a is made to correspond with the *pair* of positive integers $a+1$ and 1. (This is, of course, consistent with the usual rules of algebra.)

Finally, having laid down the rules for operating with the new numbers "$a-b$", and having shown that they are generalizations of the positive integers, it is time to show that they obey the assumptions laid down in Chapter 3 for the positive integers. Thus a result to be proved is

THEOREM 2: $(a-b)+(c-d)=(c-d)+(a-b)$, the commutative law for addition.

That is, while this law has been *assumed* for the *positive* integers, it can now be *proved* for the new generalization of the positive integers on the basis of Definitions 2 and 3 as follows:

STEPS	REASONS
1. $(a-b)+(c-d)=(a+c)-(b+d)$	Definition 2
2. $(c-d)+(a-b)=(c+a)-(d+b)$	Definition 2
3. But $a+c=c+a$, $b+d=d+b$	Assumption 3 for positive integers
4. Hence $(a+c)-(b+d)=(c+a)-(d+b)$	Substituting equals for equals [3]

$$Q.E.D.$$

---

[3] Compare footnote on Theorem 1 and see Appendix for a discussion of "substituting equals for equals" and a rigorous proof of this theorem.

Similarly, the associative law for addition, the associative and commutative laws for multiplication, and the distributive law for multiplication with respect to addition may be proved—all by reference to the definitions just made concerning the symbol $a - b$ and the assumptions made in Chapter 3 concerning the positive integers. In particular, note that the "mysterious" high-school algebra rule of "a minus times a minus is a plus" turns out to be a consequence of *Definition* 3, since $(1 - 2) \times (1 - 2) = (1 \times 1 + 2 \times 2) - (1 \times 2 + 1 \times 2) = (1 + 4) - (2 + 2) = 5 - 4$, i.e., $(-1) \times (-1) = (+1)$.

To emphasize again that this is a concept which, while very familiar to us today, is still one which is essentially an abstraction, note that the early Hindu mathematicians who first used negative numbers called them "imaginary" and used them in only a formal sense. No physical meaning was attached to negative numbers for several centuries after their introduction. And it was this lack of a physical interpretation that delayed their complete acceptance by mathematicians who, in those days, were not so inclined to the abstract as they are today.

As for zero. Turn back to the general equation, $x + b = a$, and recall that a positive solution exists for b less than a and a negative (imaginary?) solution has been invented for b greater than a. What is the solution for $a = b$? Clearly, still another invention is needed—the concept of $b - b$, or, as customarily written, 0. We may then prove that this "invented" zero possesses the properties of the zero of ordinary arithmetic. Thus, by Definition 2,

$$(c - d) + (b - b) = (c + b) - (d + b).$$

But by Definition 1, $(c + b) - (d + b) = c - d$. Hence zero added to any number does not change the value of the number. Also, by Definition 3,

$$(c - d) \times (b - b) = (c \times b + d \times b) - (c \times b + d \times b),$$

or, if we let $c \times b + d \times b = e$, $e - e$ or zero. Thus the product of any number by zero is zero.

At this point we have completed (or indicated how completion may be attained) the development of the system of integers and may ask what other assumptions, if any, besides those of Chapter 3, are satisfied by this enlarged system. That is, it is evident by Definitions 2 and 3 that we have closure (the first two assumptions); and it has been stated that the commutative, associative, and distributive laws (the next five assumptions) hold in the enlarged system.[4] On the other hand, not all the remaining assumptions, 8 to 11, can also hold. If they did, we would contradict our previous statement that essentially only the ordinary whole numbers satisfy all eleven assumptions.

First of all, then, Assumption 8 still holds for the enlarged family since $(1 + a) - a$ is a unit for the integers because of our definitions, the commutative and associative laws of addition for positive integers, the distributive law for positive integers, and the property of 1 for positive integers. For

$$[(1+a) - a] \times (c - d) = [(1+a) \times c + a \times d]$$
$$- [(1+a) \times d + a \times c] = [(c + a \times c) + a \times d]$$
$$- [(d + a \times d) + a \times c].$$

(Note the use of the distributive law and the fact that $1 \times d = d$.) But $[(c + a \times c) + a \times d] - [(d + a \times d) + a \times c] = c - d$ by Definition 1 and the commutative and associative laws of addition for positive integers.

Furthermore, the first part of the cancellation laws (that for addition) still holds, but in the second (multiplicative) part we must add the restriction that $c \neq 0$. That is, we have

THEOREM 3: For all integers a, b, and c, if $a \times c = b \times c$ and $c \neq 0$, then $a = b$.

---

[4] In fact, the commutative law for addition has been proved as Theorem 2 and the proof of the commutative law of multiplication is included in the problems at the end of the chapter.

(The restriction $c \neq 0$ is necessary, since, for example, $2 \times 0 = 3 \times 0$ but $2 \neq 3$.)

The next theorem is a consequence of Theorem 3 and is important in that it describes a property that frequently is *not* possessed by sets of numbers which will be described later.

THEOREM 4: If the product of two integers is zero, one or both of the integers must be zero. That is, $a \times b = 0$ implies that a and/or b is zero.

Let us continue with our discussion of the validity of Assumptions 8 to 11 for the integers. If we consider only the pairs $a - b$ for which a is greater than b, we have a set of quantities abstractly identical (isomorphic) with the positive integers; hence this *sub*set of the integers then satisfies Assumption 10. As an entire class, however, the integers do *not* satisfy Assumption 10. For example, the set of integers

$$-1, 0, 1, 2, 3, 4, \cdots$$

contains 1; and if it contains n, it does contain $n + 1$. But it does not include *all* the integers, for example, -2.

Finally, Assumption 11 is not satisfied, since, for example, if $a = 3$, $b = 5$, we have an x ($= 2$) such that $a + x = b$ ($3 + 2 = 5$) *and* also a y ($= -2$) such that $a = b + y$ ($3 = 5 + (-2)$), whereas Assumption 11 demands that only *one* of these possibilities holds. In place of Assumption 11, however, we have

THEOREM 5: For any two integers a and b, there is an integer x such that $a + x = b$.

For example, if $a = 3$ and $b = 5$, $x = 2$ since $3 + 2 = 5$; if $a = 5$ and $b = 3$, $x = -2$ since $5 + (-2) = 3$; and if $a = 5$ and $b = 5$, $x = 0$ since $5 + 0 = 5$.

Finally, in order to complete the "theory of signed whole numbers", note now that the omission of any discussion of subtraction can be justified by defining $(a - b) - (c - d)$ to be equal to $(a - b) + (d - c)$. This, the reader may recall, is actually what is done in elementary algebra through the medium of the rule: "To subtract x from y, change the sign of x and *add* the result to y." For example, $(2 - 3)$ $- (1 - 4) = (2 - 3) + (4 - 1) = (2 + 4) - (3 + 1) =$ $6 - 4$; i.e., $(-1) - (-3) = (-1) + (+3) = (+2)$.

It has been seen that the concept of negative numbers is indispensable for the generality of statements concerning algebraic equations. As another illustration of this fact, contrast the work of the last outstanding Greek mathematician Diophantus ($c.$ A.D. 100) with the work of the Hindu mathematician Bhāskara (A.D. 1114–1185?). Diophantus specifically rejected negative roots of quadratic equations, and he held that the equation $x^2 - x - 6 = 0$ had only one root, $x = 3$. Bhāskara, on the other hand, was quite willing to admit $x = -2$ as the other root, and hence he could say, in general, that if a quadratic equation has one root, it has two roots.[5] It is true that Bhāskara says that ". . . the second value $[-2]$ is in this case not to be taken, for it is inadequate; people do not approve of negative roots". However, this bow to public opinion was probably made with tongue in cheek, and certainly Hindu mathematicians continued to use negative numbers, regardless of the public's opinion of them. Notice, however, that while a "real" meaning seems to be necessary for common acceptance of a new kind of number, I am trying here to reverse the historical process and point out that in the last analysis, even positive integers, as well as negative integers, are only abstract entities.

In the transmission of Hindu knowledge to Europe through the Arabs, very little new was added, and by 1545 the Italian Hieronimo Cardan (1501–1576), used negative

---

[5] In Chapter 8 another extension of the number system will be made which will enable the mathematician to say that a quadratic equation *always* has two roots. Without this extension he would have to say that the equation $x^2 + 1 = 0$ has *no* roots.

numbers, although he still regarded them as fictitious. Signor
Cardan will be met again in Chapter 8, since he was one of
the first to take the next bold step of accepting square roots
of negative numbers as solutions of equations and thus pave
the way for a complete theory. That Cardan was not the
most timid algebraist of his time is shown by the work of the
eminent English algebraist Thomas Harriot (1560–1621),
who rejected negative roots entirely. In fact, according to
the historian of mathematics Florian Cajori, the majority of
the outstanding English algebraists prior to the seventeenth
century had not quite risen to the views taken by the Hindus.
The Frenchman René Descartes (1596–1650) seems to have
been the first to make *systematic* use of negative numbers,
but subsequent mathematicians frequently did not emulate
him. It was not until the middle of the nineteenth century
that the subject of negative numbers was adequately treated
in some school algebras. Even today the reasoning behind
the rules for operating with negative numbers—particularly
"a minus times a minus is a plus"—is incorrectly or inade-
quately explained in many textbooks. And recently some
writers in our leading journal on the teaching of high-school
mathematics got this matter into such a thoroughly confused
state by concentrating almost entirely on the question of ease
of presentation that a mathematician felt compelled to step
in and straighten them out.

Problems

1. Develop the system of the set of whole numbers modulo 3
where numbers are called equal if they have the same remainders
upon division by 3. (See Chapter 4.)

2. What theorems are violated by the system of integers modulo 4 that are not violated by the system of integers modulo 3?

3. $3 - 4 = 2 - ?$

4. $(1 - 2) + (1 - 4) = ?$; $(2 - 3) + (2 - 5) = ?$

5. $(1 - 2) \times (1 - 4) = ?$; $(2 - 3) \times (2 - 5) = ?$

6. Prove that $(a - b) \times (c - d) = (c - d) \times (a - b)$. What
law is this?

Chapter 6

FRACTIONS ARE EASY NOW

I T APPEARS likely that with the dawn of the concept of a
whole number there also arose a primitive concept of a
fraction. It is certainly known that the Babylonians and
Egyptians treated fractions extensively. But even the ordinary manipulation of fractions has been a source of difficulty
from ancient times down to the present. The modern school-
boy who prefers working with the awkward decimal .66666
$\cdots$ to the simple fraction $\frac{2}{3}$ would get plenty of sympathy
from first-rate mathematicians of bygone ages. To observe
the devious routes through which the human intellect plods
to reach the most modest goals, consider that the Egyptians
of 1600 B.C. reduced all their fractions (except, curiously
enough, $\frac{2}{3}$) to sums of "unit" fractions before computing with
them. (A unit fraction is one which has 1 in the numerator.)
Try to imagine a people carrying out the really difficult task
of devising rules for changing all fractions to sums of unit
fractions $\left(\text{e.g., } \frac{3}{4} = \frac{1}{2} + \frac{1}{4}, \frac{31}{30} = \frac{1}{2} + \frac{1}{3} + \frac{1}{5} \right)$ and then
deriving rules for computing with unit fractions instead of
working out our present "universal" rules for computing with
all fractions. But again, hindsight can never take the place
of foresight, and these questions of development will not be
considered further here. For our question is: How can fractions be described on a postulational basis as extensions of
the concept of integers?

Once again there appears the distinction between the concrete and the abstract. We must distinguish between an "applied" fraction and a "pure" fraction in the sense that ⅔ of a length of wire means that the wire is divided up into three equal parts and two of these parts are taken. But on the other hand, ⅔ of an integer can certainly have only an abstract meaning, since the concept of an integer is itself undefined.

The mathematician faces the situation squarely by concentrating his attention on the *operations* with the pairs of integers a/b $\left(\text{or } \dfrac{a}{b} \right)$, where a and b are integers with $b \neq 0$.[1]

Of course, as in the case of the integers, he has a motivation behind the rules he sets up. For as he wanted the properties of the positive integers to be mirrored by the properties of the positive whole numbers, and the properties of the integers (i.e., the symbols $a - b$) to be mirrored by the properties of the signed whole numbers (i.e., the signed numbers used in algebra), he wants, here, the properties of these "pure" fractions to be mirrored by the properties of their "applied" cousins. Again the important point is that every definition and proof will be referred to "first principles", i.e., the positive integers, as was done in the treatment of the integers.

First, equality is defined by

DEFINITION 1: Two (abstract) fractions a/b and c/d are said to be equal if $a \times d = b \times c$.

For example, it is true that the fraction ⅔ is equal to the fraction 4/6, not because of any meaning we must apply to ⅔ and 4/6 but because 2 (i.e., a) times 6 (d) is equal to 3 (b) times 4 (c). To repeat. It is not necessary to have a physical interpretation for fractions in order to find out whether or

---

[1] A reason for this restriction will be given later.

not two fractions are equal, and the criterion for equality is one which involves working with integers alone.

DEFINITION 2: The product $\frac{a}{b} \times \frac{c}{d}$ of two fractions $\frac{a}{b}$ and $\frac{c}{d}$ is defined to be the fraction $\frac{a \times c}{b \times d}$.

For example, $\frac{2}{3} \times \frac{5}{7} = \frac{2 \times 5}{3 \times 7} = \frac{10}{21}$. Again an operation is referred to the integers.

And now

THEOREM 6: $\frac{a}{b} \times \frac{c}{d} = \frac{c}{d} \times \frac{a}{b}$.

That is, while the commutative law for multiplication for *positive integers* must be *assumed*, it can be *proved* for *fractions* on the basis of the assumptions for positive integers and Definition 2.

Proof:

STEPS	REASONS
1. $\frac{a}{b} \times \frac{c}{d} = \frac{a \times c}{b \times d}$	Definition 2
2. $\frac{c}{d} \times \frac{a}{b} = \frac{c \times a}{d \times b}$	Definition 2
3. Hence $\frac{a}{b} \times \frac{c}{d} = \frac{c}{d} \times \frac{a}{b}$	
if $\frac{a \times c}{b \times d} = \frac{c \times a}{d \times b}$	By Steps 1 and 2
4. But $\frac{a \times c}{b \times d} = \frac{c \times a}{d \times b}$	
since $a \times c = c \times a$, $b \times d = d \times b$	Assumption 4

Q.E.D.[2]

---

[2] Actually, an "extended" form of Assumption 4 is being used, since a, b, c, and d may be negative as well as positive. However, the proof that this assumption holds for negative integers (see Chapter 5, problem 6) is made on the basis of the assumption for the positive integers.

Let us at this point note that there are significant omissions and changes in our treatment of fractions from that given in regular advanced texts, just as there were in our treatment of the integers. Thus, first of all, the mathematician uses, again, the symbol (a, b) for this new pair. Secondly, the invariance of our definition of multiplication under the equality relation has been omitted. That is, in a complete treatment we would show that if $a/b = a'/b'$ and $c/d = c'/d'$, then $(a/b) \times (c/d) = (a'/b') \times (c'/d')$. Finally, we should, of course, make a definition for the addition of fractions in terms of addition and multiplication of integers (with proof of invariance) and show that the commutative law of addition, the associative laws, and the distributive law hold. We may also show that we have a unit, a/a, and we may verify that Theorems 3 to 5 of the previous chapter hold, with the word "integer" replaced by "fraction". It seems to me, however, that such details at this point would be somewhat out of place in a general survey of this type. Some of these points are treated further in the Appendix.

The final step, however, should certainly not be omitted. This is the remark that the number system has actually been extended by virtue of

DEFINITION 3: $a/1$ corresponds to a.

(Cf. $(a + 1) - 1$ corresponds to a.)

That is, after making this definition, the mathematician can assert that he is not talking about just a new class of objects called fractions,[3] which have some of the same properties as the integers, but about a class of objects which *includes* the integers as a special case. For it is clear that the fraction $a/1$ "behaves" just like the integer a with respect

---

[3] Perhaps it would be well to remark here that decimals provide us with just another way of *writing* fractions, not with a new type of number. Thus, $1.2 = 1\frac{2}{10} = \frac{6}{5}$; $.01 = \frac{1}{100}$; etc.

to multiplication (and addition, too, under the definition not stated).

The concept of a fraction dates back thousands of years, and fractions are mentioned in some of the earliest manuscripts extant, such as the Rhind Papyrus (*c.* 1650 B.C.). To this date, however, they have never been very "popular". As remarked before, the early Egyptians confined themselves almost entirely to fractions with numerator 1 and expressed other fractions as sums of these unit fractions. This obstinacy continued for some time and historians find that the Greek mathematician Heron (*c.* A.D. 100) still used unit fractions more often than the general type. But the Hindus not only used fractions of all kinds around A.D. 600, but introduced the notation we now use; for example, $\frac{2}{3}$ for two-thirds (except that they omitted the bar). This latter refinement was used sporadically by the Arabs and came into general use in Western Europe only in the sixteenth century. The minor variation of the slant bar, or solidus, was introduced around 1880 by C. G. Stokes, largely because of the difficulty of printing fractions in the usual way.[4] The word "fraction", itself, is comparatively new. As late as the sixteenth century writers often used the term "broken number" (as we use *whole* number for integer even today).

The struggle to systematize and make simple the rules of operations with fractions might be said to continue up to the present day; but fortunately such mundane details need not be considered here. It should be noted, however, that the omission of any discussion of division along with multiplication can now be justified. For the result of dividing *a* by

---

[4] Thus Cayley (see Chapter 9) wrote Stokes: "I think the 'solidus' looks very well indeed . . . ; it would give you a strong claim to be President of a Society for the Prevention of Cruelty to Printers." A surprising amount of mathematical notation has been modified because of such humane considerations—as well as with a due regard for the extra expense of hand-set type!

b may be written as a/b or $a \times (1/b)$. That is, division of the integer a by the integer b is equivalent to the multiplication of a $(= a/1)$ by $1/b$. (Cf. the reason for the omission of any discussion of subtraction given in Chapter 5.) Our original restriction that $b \neq 0$ in a/b is now seen to be related to the fact that division by zero is impossible. For if we were entitled to use zero in the denominator of a fraction, we would be defining, for example, 6 divided by 0. Now if $6 \div 0 = b$, we would have $0 \times b = 6$ (just as $6 \div 2 = 3$ means that $2 \times 3 = 6$). But we know that $0 \times b = 0$ (see Chapter 4), and hence division by zero is excluded.[5]

Here is a good place for a sixth-inning stretch before going on to treat of matters which lie beyond what might be called the "self-evident" numbers ("rational" is the technical term used). For as has been shown, the cave man undoubtedly had a perception of the concept of a whole number. The most primitive tribes have invented a series of grunts for the numbers one and two at least, and fractions were probably one of the unrecorded plagues that Moses visited upon the Egyptians. Furthermore, a bright, observant preschool child picks up some idea of these concepts without formal training because of his living in a scientific (and hence mathematical) age. It is true that negative numbers, which were not formally acknowledged as legitimate numbers of the number family until around the time of Columbus, have also been discussed. But once the idea of a negative number *is* presented, many obvious uses for it are found in connection with temperatures, debts, and other common, concrete ideas of modern life.

Such a firm contact with the everyday experiences of mankind will begin to be relinquished in the next chapter, with

---

[5] To be perfectly honest with the reader, I should acknowledge that this seems like a good place to "invent" a new kind of number to take care of this situation. To a certain *limited* extent, this can be and is done. But it would take us far afield to go into this matter here.

the introduction of irrational numbers which, as will be shown, startled the mature and sophisticated Greeks of Plato's time. And this contact with common experience will increasingly diminish until, in the last chapters, it may seem that we are standing with both feet planted firmly in mid-air.

What, then, has been accomplished in the first six chapters? Primarily I have not been concerned with explaining abstractions, but rather I have been pointing out that what the reader considers as concrete must be considered as abstract if he is to have any prospect of comprehending the abstractions to come. To accomplish this aim of "making easy mathematics hard", two approaches have been used. First of all, by showing that the "obvious" of today was the major invention of yesterday, I hope to have convinced the reader that the ideas of whole numbers, fractions, and negative numbers, together with the operations of addition and multiplication, are by no means instinctive, and that the relative ease with which we acquire such ideas today is due to the fact that we are capitalizing on the struggles of generations past to achieve a mastery over number. As the eminent mathematician A. N. Whitehead puts it:

> Before the introduction of the Arabic notation, multiplication was difficult, and the division even of integers called into play the highest mathematical faculties. Probably nothing in the modern world could have more astonished a Greek mathematician than to learn that, under the influence of compulsory education, the whole population of Western Europe, from the highest to the lowest, could perform the operation of division for the largest numbers. This fact would have seemed to him a sheer impossibility. . . . Our modern power of easy reckoning with decimal fractions is the most miraculous result of the gradual discovery of a perfect notation.

Secondly, by showing that there exist other quantities besides ordinary numbers, such as vectors and point sets, which have many (although not all) of the properties of our garden variety of numbers, it is seen that an abstract approach via *properties* of numbers is very illuminating. In other words, once it is realized that the words "positive integer" may well be left undefined and attention confined to the question of what to do with them, we find a throng of eager candidates for the title of "positive integer"—so many, in fact, that it is only by putting severe restrictions on the operations that the field can be reserved for, essentially, the abstract equivalents of the ordinary whole numbers.

One more comment concerning procedure before we leave terra firma. The reader may have wondered why I did not undertake to motivate the introduction of fractions, as I did negative numbers, by pointing out that, for example, the equation $2x = 6$ has the solution $x = 6 \div 2 = 3$, and hence, in generalizing, invent the symbol $\frac{2}{3}$ as the solution for the equation $3x = 2$. There are two reasons for not proceeding in this way. First of all, the concept of a fraction undoubtedly arose long before the solution of equations was considered. Secondly, whenever a mathematical concept is considered which is in such general circulation that it has become a commonplace, I want to present it in a different way so as to make sure that the reader will realize the essentially abstract nature of the concept.

PROBLEMS

1. Determine, by means of Definition 1, whether or not $\frac{3}{4} = \frac{6}{8}$, $\frac{1}{3} = \frac{2}{5}$, $\frac{4}{5} = \frac{12}{15}$.

2. Multiply $\frac{2}{3}$ by $\frac{4}{5}$; $\frac{1}{6}$ by $\frac{2}{3}$.

3. Prove the associative law for multiplication of fractions.

Chapter 7

THE UNSPEAKABLE

IF THE integers are, as Kronecker asserted, God's sole contribution to mathematics, the mathematician can avoid blasphemy only by referring all his notions about other numbers to the integers, just as the fundamentalist seeks justification of his biology and geology in the Bible! But should Kronecker's remark be taken seriously? After all, it was made in an after-dinner speech! In this chapter I hope to shed some light on this philosophical question without, however, providing a definitive answer.

In order to appreciate the force of Kronecker's epigram, it is necessary to go back to the time of Pythagoras, about 500 B.C. At that time, of course, the concepts of whole numbers and fractions (which, as noted, are based on whole numbers) were well known. There was, however, one important difference in the Greek mathematician's viewpoint towards the integers and that displayed in this book. Today the mathematician emphasizes the abstract character of the integers and consistently and persistently refuses to give a concrete meaning to the word "integer". Quite the contrary was true with the Pythagoreans. Not only did they regard the integers as being definitely a part of their real world, but they endowed them, as they did their gods, with human characteristics.

In view of some very recent developments in science that will be discussed later, it is pertinent to expose a few of Pythagoras' superstitions which are intermingled with his solid achievements in the manner so characteristic of much of Greek life where reason and intellect were still hard pressed by ignorance and prejudice.[1] Note then that the Pythagoreans were not content with viewing the whole numbers merely as a base for the construction of a complete system of arithmetic. Instead, they began to attribute special qualities to certain numbers. Specifically, the Pythagorean follies open with a cast of ten—the numbers 1 through 10—called the decad, with top billing being given to a quartet, called the tetrad, consisting of the numbers 1, 2, 3, and 4. The clash of the sexes, a topic common to many plays, is brought in by the simple device of calling the odd numbers male and the even numbers female.

Now let those who profess the attitude that human thought reached its pinnacle of development among the Greeks pay careful attention to the lucid arguments which follow—arguments that were accepted by a large group of influential Greeks (including Plato). First of all, the Pythagoreans showed that the male marriage number is 5. For 2 is the first female number and 3 the first male number (1 being presumably too puny for wedlock). And $2 + 3 = 5$, Q.E.D. Likewise, in marriage a female is multiplied by a male so it is easy to see that the male marriage number is $2 \times 3 = 6$. Continuing, we note that 4 is expressible as 2×2 and $2 + 2$. This expresses so clearly the concept of "an eye for an eye and a tooth for a tooth" that we are certainly forced to conclude that 4 is justice.

And so on. The whole performance is capped by a dazzling display of juggling where 1, the point; 2, the line; 3, the plane; and 4, the solid, add up to be $1 + 2 + 3 + 4 = 10$, and the tetrad rules supreme. As E. T. Bell says in his *Magic of Numbers*, "We are in a dream world where anything we wish to prove can be proved, for the sufficient reason that any obstacle to strict deduction may be abolished by intro-

---

[1] Not that such a criticism is uniquely applicable to the Greeks! But in admiring the brilliant achievements of Hellenic culture, we tend to overlook, it seems to me, its shortcomings. Hence this comment.

ducing as a new postulate the nonexistence of the obstacle."

Now the trend of scientific development from the Renaissance on has been away from this type of mental-moral gymnastics so that one could, until recently, believe that numerology and number mysticism were in a class with voodoo and a belief in witches. But certain modern physicists seem to be reviving this reverence for whole numbers and without, of course, imputing moral qualities to them, they are predicating hypotheses concerning the physical universe on the basis of arguments that certain physical constants "ought" to have integral values. In fact, Pascual Jordan, one of the founders of modern quantum mechanics, recently made some elaborate and daring cosmological conjectures on the basis of the fact that certain numerical combinations of fundamental physical constants (such as the speed of light) have the approximate value 1.

Whether this "moralized mathematics" is to become a common practice in years to come, or whether our descendants will laugh at these conjectures as we do at those of Pythagoras, is certainly not a matter that can be decided today. One thing is certain: already amateur philosophers have seized upon the physicist's "principle of uncertainty" and used it to "prove" all sorts of things concerning religion and morals. Hence the consequences of the spread of the information that a species of numerology has its place in serious physics are fearful to contemplate!

But to return to the present story. When Kronecker spoke his piece, he was not, obviously, advocating a return to the superstitions of ancient Greece but was simply insisting that the structure of mathematics be built on the basis of a minimum number of undefined terms. That is, while positive integers must be accepted here as undefined, it would be logically uneconomical to build up a theory of negative integers and fractions without reference to the positive integers. The question still in dispute today is this: How far can one go in developing mathematics on such a basis without also developing academic sterility? So far as our story goes, we *have* based our study on positive integers so far [2] —but let us see what now comes up.

With this brief sketch of the Pythagorean attitude towards numbers in mind, the reader is asked to invest himself with just a little of this mysticism in order that he may attain some appreciation of the loathing of the Pythagoreans for the "unspeakable" number that they found they were nurturing in their midst. It was born, in fact, of the famous "Pythagorean theorem"—one of the most important of plane geometry. This theorem, the reader may recall, states that the sum of the squares on the sides of a right triangle is equal to the square on the hypotenuse. Its proof, of course, involves only the concepts of geometry and not those of arithmetic. However, it is capable of an arithmetic interpretation. As a special case, consider the isosceles right triangle with sides of unit length as shown below. Then by the Pythagorean

theorem, the hypotenuse, c, must satisfy the equation

$$c^2 = 1^2 + 1^2 = 1 + 1 = 2 \quad \text{or} \quad c = \sqrt{2}.$$

That is, if the Pythagoreans are to continue to operate with fractions alone, they must produce a fraction, $\dfrac{a}{b}$, such

---

[2] Please recall, however, that I have remarked that other number systems may be described in a similar fashion by undefined terms and assumptions without prior consideration of the positive integers. It is common, in fact, to first consider the entire set of integers and then obtain the positive integers as a subset of the integers. Thus the postulational method is more than just a tool to "get started" on this one particular mathematical journey. It is a powerful general machinery for mathematical investigations.

that $\dfrac{a}{b} \times \dfrac{a}{b} = 2$. For it certainly must be admitted that the hypotenuse has a very concrete length and hence should be capable of exact measurement. Now how can it be proved that $\sqrt{2}$ is *not* the square of a fraction? In Pythagoras' time and today it is done by the *reductio ad absurdum* type of argument used so frequently in elementary geometry. In other words, it is assumed that $\sqrt{2}$ *is* the square of a fraction and then it is shown that this assumption leads to an absurdity; hence the assumption must be false.

Before the proof is given, however, consider how I should have liked, for the sake of continuity of development, to have the concept of irrational numbers, such as $\sqrt{2}$, arise out of algebraic symbolism. In this fictitious situation, picture an ancient algebraist studying the solution of equations of the form

$$x^2 = c,$$

where c is a positive whole number, just as he was imagined as studying $x + 4 = 5$, etc. in Chapter 5. If $c = 1$, he would say that $x = 1$ (the idea of the other solution, $x = -1$, not yet being conceived). If $c = 4$, then $x = 2$; etc. However, upon taking $c = 2$, he would find a very real difficulty. For no matter what fractions he might try as values of x (and fractions would be all that he would know about), he would find that the square of no one of them would yield 2. For example, $\left(\dfrac{14}{10}\right)^2 = \left(\dfrac{7}{5}\right)^2 = \dfrac{49}{25}$ is less than 2; $\left(\dfrac{141}{100}\right)^2 = \dfrac{19{,}881}{10{,}000}$ is closer to, but still less than 2. Better and better *approximations* to $\sqrt{2}$ can be made (by, for example, the usual arithmetic process of extracting a square root), but a fraction can *never* be found whose square is *exactly* 2.

How can it be stated categorically that no fraction can ever be found? After all, no matter how many fractions are tried, there are always others left that haven't been tried and that might conceivably work. The proof that *no* fraction will work is a very elegant one and may have been given first by Pythagoras himself. As mentioned before, the proof is of the *reductio ad absurdum* type. That is, it is shown that the assumption that $\sqrt{2}$ is a fraction leads to a false statement. All right, suppose then that

$$x = \frac{a}{b}, \quad x^2 = 2,$$

where a and b are positive integers *not both even*. The assumption that a and b are not both even is no restriction, for if x is the quotient of two even integers, it is also the quotient of two integers, one of which, at least, is *not* even. For example, if $x = \frac{14}{10}$, x is also equal to $\frac{7}{5}$; if $x = \frac{16}{10}$, x is also equal to $\frac{8}{5}$; etc. It is then shown that the assumption that $x^2 = 2$ implies that both a and b *are* even, and hence the assumption must be false. For if $x^2 = 2$,

$$x^2 = \left(\frac{a}{b}\right)^2 = \frac{a^2}{b^2} = 2$$

so that

$$a^2 = 2b^2.$$

Thus a^2 is certainly even. But can the square of an odd number ever be even ($3^2 = 9$, $5^2 = 25$, etc.)? Clearly not (this fact can be rigorously proved, by the way). Hence a^2 even implies that a is even. But the "evenness" of a implies $a = 2d$, where d is an integer ($4 = 2 \times 2$, $6 = 2 \times 3$, etc.). But then

$$a^2 = (2d)^2 = 4d^2 = 2b^2,$$

so that $b^2 = 2d^2$; and hence, by the same argument as used for a, b is also even. Thus there emerges the desired contradiction to the assumption that $\left(\dfrac{a}{b}\right)^2 = 2$, since it could be assumed that at least one of a and b were *odd*.

And so the Pythagoreans found the "unspeakable" (*alogon* in Greek) number beyond the fractions. What to do about it? The brotherhood, horrified by the existence of such a creature, attempted to keep it a trade secret—to the extent, so legend has it, of arranging a shipwreck for one of their group who divulged it to the uninitiated. Obviously, it seemed to them, the existence of such a number as $\sqrt{2}$ completely wrecked their plans to run the universe through integers. But today the secret is certainly out, and mathematicians must face up to it. Must they, then, abandon the attempt to carry on their extensions of the number system via the integers? Kronecker apparently felt that way, for he remarked to C. L. F. Lindeman, when everyone was congratulating the latter on his proof that *pi* (another number that is not a fraction) is "transcendental" (see below), "Of what value is your beautiful proof, since irrational [nonfractional] numbers do not exist?".

Now there *are* two common ways of defining these new numbers in terms of fractions (and hence, ultimately, in terms of integers). One of these methods, due to J. W. R. Dedekind (1831–1916) is presented briefly in the Appendix. The other, due to G. Cantor (1845–1918), brings in the important idea of *completeness*. As an illustration of this idea, consider first the sequence of sums

$$1,\ 1+\tfrac{1}{2},\ 1+\tfrac{1}{2}+\tfrac{1}{4},\ 1+\tfrac{1}{2}+\tfrac{1}{4}+\tfrac{1}{8},\ \cdots$$

which approaches closer and closer to the number 2. That is, by adding on more and more terms to the sum (as $1/16$, $1/32$, etc.) we can get just as close to 2 as we like. Briefly, we say that the *infinite series*

$$1+\frac{1}{2}+\frac{1}{4}+\frac{1}{8}+\cdots$$

is *convergent* and has 2 as a *limit*.[3] Now *if* all convergent series with fractions (including, of course, whole numbers) as terms had a fractional value as a limit, we would say that the set of fractional (or *rational*) numbers was *complete*. This, however, is not the case. For example, consider the sequence of numbers

$$1, \frac{1}{2}, \frac{1}{2} \times \frac{1}{4}, \frac{1}{2} \times \frac{1}{4} \times \frac{3}{6}, \frac{1}{2} \times \frac{1}{4} \times \frac{3}{6} \times \frac{5}{8}, \frac{1}{2} \times \frac{1}{4} \times \frac{3}{6} \times \frac{5}{8} \times \frac{7}{10},$$

etc. Form a series from these numbers by alternately adding and subtracting as follows:

$$1 + \frac{1}{2} - \frac{1}{2} \times \frac{1}{4} + \frac{1}{2} \times \frac{1}{4} \times \frac{3}{6} - \frac{1}{2} \times \frac{1}{4} \times \frac{3}{6} \times \frac{5}{8}$$

$$+ \frac{1}{2} \times \frac{1}{4} \times \frac{3}{6} \times \frac{5}{8} \times \frac{7}{10} - \cdots$$

Or, simplifying,

$$1 + \frac{1}{2} - \frac{1}{8} + \frac{1}{16} - \frac{5}{128} + \frac{35}{1280} - \cdots$$

It can be shown that this series does *not* converge to a rational number but to the irrational number $\sqrt{2}$.[4]

So we now have new numbers defined by such series which are called *real* numbers. It is then possible to define addition and multiplication of these series in such a way that the laws previously indicated as holding for the rational numbers will hold for the real numbers or series. Furthermore, these new numbers include the rational numbers as special cases, since, for example,

$$2 = 2 + 0 + 0 + 0 + \cdots$$

---

[3] More precisely, we say that a series $a_1 + a_2 + a_3 + \cdots$ has a limit S if for every positive number *e*, no matter how small, there exists a positive integer N such that for every positive integer $n > N$ the numerical difference between S and S_n ($= a_1 + \cdots + a_n$) is less than *e*.

[4] The six terms given above give $\sqrt{2}$ correct to only two figures. It is a "slow" series not suitable for actual computation.

Now the surprising thing is that if we attempt to continue this process and form new series

$$s = a_1 + a_2 + a_3 + \cdots$$

where a_1, a_2, a_3, $\cdots$ are now the newly invented real numbers, we find that there are *rational* numbers b_1, b_2, b_3, $\cdots$ such that we also have

$$s = b_1 + b_2 + b_3 + \cdots.$$

In other words, there are no gaps left to be filled in, and we speak of the real numbers as being *complete*.

This, very sketchily, is one of the ways in which one finally obtains all the numbers needed to measure distances, including, for example, such numbers as $\sqrt{2}$ and others described below. All the gaps previously existing in our scale of measurement have been filled. It should be noted, however, that neither the Dedekind nor the Cantor method of definition would be completely acceptable to Kronecker, due to the use of certain concepts which Kronecker felt should be banned from mathematics. The exact reasons are not important for our purposes, but it should perhaps be remarked that, in a somewhat modified form, the issue that Kronecker raised is still alive today, although it is only fair to state at the same time that the majority of mathematicians quietly ignore its existence. Many, in fact, feel that there is no real issue involved at all.

The only irrational numbers mentioned so far have been $\sqrt{2}$ and *pi*. However, included in the class of irrational numbers are all sorts of irrationalities as cube roots, fourth roots, and even such compound monstrosities as

$$\sqrt{\dfrac{\sqrt[3]{1+\sqrt{2}} + \sqrt[5]{10-\sqrt{2}}}{5}}$$

which do arise in the solution of more complicated equations. Furthermore, in geometry and other parts of mathematics, still another type of number arises besides these "roots" (*pi* is an example) which not only is not a fraction but also is not a combination of "roots". Such numbers, however, called *transcendental* numbers,[5] do not arise in the solution of "ordinary" algebraic equations [6] (such as $x^2 + 3x + 1 = 0$, $3x^3 - 3x^2 - 2x + 5 = 0$, etc.). Hence they need not be considered here.

Noting once again that it has been found necessary, or at least desirable, to use some of the language of algebra in describing the evolution of the number concept, I believe it is pertinent to sketch now the development of the part of algebra which is used here, to prepare the way for the culminating achievements in the "theory of equations" to be described in the next chapter.

First of all, vastly different dates can be assigned to the beginnings of algebra,[7] depending upon one's definition of the term. Historians of mathematics commonly divide algebra into three kinds: the *rhetorical,* the *syncopated,* and the *symbolic.* In rhetorical algebra, no symbols are used. It deserves the title of algebra only because the ancient problems, considered as early as 2000 B.C., are similar to the word problems worked today by high-school students. For example, the famous Rhind papyrus, written by Ahmose sometime before 1600 B.C. and believed by some historians to be founded on an earlier work dating back as far as 3000 B.C., gives this problem: "Divide 100 loaves among 5 persons; $\frac{1}{7}$ of what the first three get is what the last two get. What

---

[5] Technically, the term "irrational number" includes both numbers such as $\sqrt{2}$ and numbers such as *pi.* The special class of irrational numbers considered here are called "real algebraic numbers".

[6] By "ordinary algebraic equation" is meant any equation of the form $a_0x^n + a_1x^{n-1} + \cdots + a_{n-1}x + a_n = 0$, where the coefficients $a_0, a_1, \cdots a_{n-1}, a_n$ are positive or negative integers or zero.

[7] The word algebra itself comes from the Arabic word *algabr* for *reduction,* which was used in the same sense as we use *transposition,* i.e., the shifting of the terms of an equation from one side to the other.

is the difference?" This is a problem in what are called arithmetic progressions today. However, Ahmose's solution is nonsymbolic and he probably used what is called "the rule of false position". At least this is the viewpoint of the distinguished historian Moritz Cantor, in view of the cryptic remarks that Ahmose offers as a solution: "Make the difference $5\frac{1}{2}$; 23, $17\frac{1}{2}$, 12, $6\frac{1}{2}$, 1. Multiply by $1\frac{2}{3}$; $38\frac{1}{3}$, $29\frac{1}{6}$, 20, $10\frac{2}{3}$ $\frac{1}{6}$ †, $1\frac{2}{3}$." Just what the rule of false position is need not concern us here. I remark only that it is a nonsymbolic way of handling algebra which maintained its popularity up through the eighteenth century. It has been entirely replaced by the symbolic methods today, and most contemporary mathematicians are only vaguely acquainted with the method.

In syncopated algebra there is an incomplete use of symbols, together with words. For example, Vieta, in the sixteenth century, wrote the equation

a cubus $+ b$ in a quadr. $3 + a$ in b quadr. $3 + b$ cubo
aequalia $\overline{a + b}$ *cubo*

which, in symbolic algebra, looks like this:

$$a^3 + 3a^2b + 3ab^2 + b^3 = (a+b)^3.$$

A complete story of our present-day symbolism is a long one indeed, and for each symbol $(+, \times, -,$ etc.) several pages would be needed.[8] Not only were the present symbols slow in coming, but many less suitable ones were used by certain mathematicians and later discarded (for example, the notations of Newton for the derivative).

---

† Recall (Chapter 6) that the Egyptians used only unit fractions, with the exception of $\frac{2}{3}$. Thus $\frac{2}{3}$ $\frac{1}{6}$ meant $\frac{2}{3} + \frac{1}{6}$ or $\frac{5}{6}$. Note, by the way, that $38\frac{1}{3} - 29\frac{1}{6} = 29\frac{1}{6} - 20 = 20 - 10\frac{2}{3} = 10\frac{2}{3} - 1\frac{2}{3} = 9\frac{1}{6}$ (i.e., an arithmetic progression), while $\frac{1}{7}(38\frac{1}{3} + 29\frac{1}{6} + 20) = 10\frac{2}{3} + 1\frac{2}{3}$. He's right!

[8] See Florian Cajori, *History of Mathematical Notation*, Vol. I, La Salle (Illinois): The Open Court Publishing Co., 1928.

It is generally agreed that the first exponent of a thorough-going symbolism was Franciscus Vieta. Although his own suggestions were not generally carried out, his proposals were seriously considered. Thus it was not long after his time that algebra came to have the form so detested by the students of today who look upon the symbolism as an obstacle to the handling of problems and who, therefore, always prefer to work with the smallest amount of symbolism possible.

In view of the last remark, it would be well to consider here the importance of symbolism in the development of mathematics. Unfortunately, algebraic symbolism is usually introduced to the student as a sort of "shorthand". That is, it is remarked at the beginning of most elementary algebra books that such a statement as "length times width is equal to the area of a rectangle" can be written as $l \times w = A$. But while it is undoubtedly true that symbols first arose in an attempt to make more concise the writing of mathematical statements, the importance of the use of symbols is not primarily the shortening of time in writing down a statement, the space saved, or even the fact that, by so writing it, the statement is made easier to grasp. (Compare the statement "Find a number such that twice the number added to 5 yields 15" with the corresponding symbolic statement "$2x + 5 = 15$". In other words, the study of "word" problems in an algebra course is the most difficult part for the average student.)

What, then, *are* the main contributions of symbolic notation? This is a matter of some controversy. Personally, I feel that the use of symbols tends to bring out the essentially abstract nature of mathematics and that mathematics without symbolism would not advance very far. This point of view is shared by many well-known mathematicians. On the other hand, many equally eminent mathematicians firmly believe that symbols are an aid in focusing attention upon the abstract nature of mathematics only because of the lucidity they bring about in their role as abbreviations. I shall not try to debate this point here.

No matter how one may feel, however, about the role of symbols as devices for fostering the development of concepts and theorems, there is little question but that it is far easier to prove theorems concerning operations with numbers by the use of symbols than it is to prove them verbally. As a random sample of this sort of thing, consider the simple algebraic identity of the type discussed in elementary algebra:

$$5 (2x + 1) + y + 6 = 10 (x + 1) + (y + 1).$$

"Translated" into lay language, this becomes a mystifying trick to the uninitiated: "Take two numbers each less than nine (say 4 and 7). Multiply the first number by 2, $(2 \times 4 = 8)$ and add 1 $(8 + 1 = 9)$. Multiply by 5, $(5 \times 9 = 45)$, and to this result add the second number and then 6, $(45 + 7 + 6 = 58)$. From this result the two numbers taken may be obtained, $(5 - 1 = 4, 8 - 1 = 7)$."

The most important role, however, that symbols play here is that of generalizing the concept of numbers. It is this role that I wish to stress. To sketch out very rapidly the development of algebra which used only the concept of positive fractions (including, of course, positive whole numbers), it will suffice to say here that considerable algebra has been found in the clay tablets of the Babylonians and a small amount in the papyri of the Egyptians. No symbols appear, but rules essentially equivalent to those given today for the solution of quadratic equations appear on a tablet dated 1800 B.C. However, the Babylonians did not introduce the negative and complex numbers that are essential to a complete treatment of the quadratic. For, as noted before, *one* of the ways in which new numbers may "force" their way into the thoughts of mathematicians is through the use of symbols.

The purely rhetorical nature of ancient mathematics perhaps tended to hide any "strange" solutions.

Again, the Greeks, while considering fairly complex problems in algebra (roughly speaking, of the type taught in a
course in intermediate high-school algebra today—plus problems in "number theory"), also did not use a symbolic notation to any extent and so missed this way of approaching
negative numbers as well as irrational numbers. They did,
however, develop an extensive theory of irrational numbers
from geometrical considerations.

Little is known about the lives of the earliest algebraists.
Ahmose, for example, is merely a name. Although many
miscellaneous results were obtained by algebraists of Babylon and Greece, attention is next centered upon Pythagoras,
since it was he who (unwillingly!) made the first extension
of the number concept beyond the fractions. I say "he".
Actually, it is very difficult to determine the exact extent of
Pythagoras' own contributions. For like Plato and Socrates,
Pythagoras had his "school" which was taught entirely by
lectures; hence he left no permanent records. Also, the students of the school were inclined to minimize their personal
roles and to ascribe all their own discoveries to the founder
of the school. Pythagoras himself was born around 540 B.C.,
probably on the island of Samos. He undoubtedly traveled
widely before he established his school in Crotona on the
southeastern coast of Italy. He absorbed considerable
knowledge (along with a good deal of mysticism) from
Egypt and Babylon. His outstanding reputation during his
lifetime continued to be enhanced for centuries after his
death by the pleasant custom of later Greek writers of as-
cribing to Pythagoras any mathematical inventions whose
inventor was unknown.

Again, from the time of Pythagoras to Vieta, many mathematicians advanced the subject of algebra as much as did
Vieta. The emphasis placed on Vieta here is due mainly to

his contributions to the highly important development of symbolism. However, he is rated as the greatest French algebraist of the sixteenth century. His greatest achievement lay in applying algebra to geometry to a larger extent and in a more systematic manner than had been done previously. Franciscus Vieta (1540–1603) was a native of Poitu, was educated as a lawyer, and spent most of his life in public service under Henry III and Henry IV. This type of nonprofessional mathematician was quite common up to the eighteenth century. Today, however, the increasing technicality of mathematics restricts advancement of the subject almost entirely to the professional.

One of Vieta's jobs during France's war with Spain in the reign of King Henry IV was to make and break codes. In our own times, too, mathematicians work at this task. But in Vieta's time the enemy did not retaliate by having his own mathematicians put to work. The Spaniards attributed to magic Vieta's breaking of one of their codes—a code containing over five hundred characters!

PROBLEM

Prove that the square root of 3 is irrational (i.e., not a fraction).

Chapter 8

THE GREAT i SOLVES ALL

IN Chapter 5 I mentioned the length of time that it took for negative numbers to be accepted into the number family. Even before the negative numbers had become fully legitimized, however, a new type of number of even more doubtful parentage forced its way into mathematics. To set the stage for its appearance, let us again consider the solution of quadratic equations—for example, the equation $x^2 + 1 = 0$, which is another special case of the general quadratic equation, $ax^2 + bx + c = 0$. ($x^2 - 2 = 0$ was considered in Chapter 7.) Clearly, before mathematicians can say that they have a complete theory of quadratic equations, they must be able to solve the general quadratic for all values of a, b, and c. Thus equations like $x^2 - 2 = 0$ forced the invention of irrational numbers, and equations like $x + 3 = 0$ forced the invention of negative numbers. Likewise, when $a = c = 1$, $b = 0$ we have $x^2 + 1 = 0$, $x^2 = -1$, which calls for the introduction of a new kind of number, denoted customarily by i, with the property that $i^2 = -1$. For if x were a positive number, its square would certainly be positive, while the square of a negative number is also positive ("minus times a minus is a plus")! This new type of number and others "like" it are called *complex numbers*.

This "mystical" quantity, i, is the source of great perplexity to the student of algebra in high-school and beginning college mathematics classes; for to him all the other numbers (integers, fractions, negative numbers, and even irrational numbers) are very obviously measures of "real" objects that he sees around him. But try as he may, he cannot find an example of i such as i dollars or i cows. Now the main object of the previous part of this book has been to put the reader into such a frame of mind that he may very placidly accept this and other new numbers. Thus he knows that the number 1 is an abstraction to start with, and, in particular, has not been defined; the number -1 is a further abstraction; $\frac{1}{2}$ likewise, and, as discussed just a short time ago, the number $\sqrt{2}$. It is true that the number 1 may be attached as an adjective to the word cow, and "one cow" + "two cows" = "three cows" is a concrete realization of the abstract statement that $1 + 2 = 3$. Furthermore, $\frac{1}{2}$ has connotations dealing with the division of a pie by two equally hungry boys; $\sqrt{2}$ is the description of the length of a certain very real line segment, and even -28 may bring a very real shiver if one imagines degrees written after it. But to repeat, the numbers 1, -1, $\frac{1}{2}$, and $\sqrt{2}$ (to which collection is now added i) are all abstractions which, if desired, may be applied to various physical situations.[1]

In other words, I hope that the reader has been enabled, by the discussion of the abstract nature of the commonplace objects of mathematical study, to accept the quantity i as an item absolutely necessary to introduce in order to carry out the announced program of solving all ordinary algebraic equations. He may be interested in a concrete realization of i as something more definite than a new kind of number whose square is -1, but his need for such a realization should be less pressing than it is for algebra students who do not have the advantage of an abstract introduction to the previous parts of the number system. Incidentally, the fact that I lay the blame for the poor reception of i to lack of preparation

---

[1] Even i, I must confess, has a physical meaning which will be mentioned later. I hope, however, that the reader will not turn to this interpretation immediately, but rather that he will accept the abstract treatment to be given now as a good introduction for the following chapter in which *hypercomplex* numbers are presented. There are also very practical applications of i in alternating-current theory.

rather than to inherent resistance to new ideas is substantiated by history. For even the great Leibnitz (whose reverent attitude toward the binary system was exposed in Chapter 1) went into unmathematical ecstasies over i, writing: "The Divine Spirit found a sublime outlet in that wonder of analysis, the portent of the ideal, that mean between being and not-being, which we call the imaginary [square] root of negative unity."

Again, as in the case with negative numbers, fractions, and irrational quantities, a complete discussion of complex numbers involves a formulation of the appropriate definitions for and operations with complex numbers and proofs that these new quantities then obey certain of the assumptions that were originally postulated for the positive integers. The development is very similar to that for negative numbers and fractions, and the reader would do well to review what was done in that connection in Chapters 5 and 6. Thus in discussing negative numbers, a *pair* of integers, a and b, was considered, written in the form $a - b$, while in discussing fractions, the pair was written a/b. The rules for operating with these pairs of numbers were then given *in terms of positive integers*, and then it was shown (or indicated) that these operations on negative numbers and fractions were subject to many of the same restrictions as the corresponding operations on positive integers (the commutative, associative, and distributive laws, and the modification of Assumption 9 discussed in Theorem 3 of Chapter 5). Finally, it was observed that the number system was actually being extended, since the signed number $(a + b) - b$ was identical in behavior with the positive integer a, and the fraction $a/1$ was identical in behavior with the integer a.

In a very similar vein, mathematicians consider complex numbers as pairs of real [2] numbers a and b, and write them

---

[2] A real number is an integer, fraction, or irrational number. That is, any of the numbers previously discussed.

in the form (a, b).[3] The three operations on these couples are described by

DEFINITION 1: $(a, b) + (c, d) = (a + c, b + d)$.

For example, $(2, 4) + (5, 6) = (7, 10)$.

DEFINITION 2: $(a, b) \times (c, d) = (a \times c - b \times d, a \times d + b \times c)$.

For example, $(2, 4) \times (5, 6) = (2 \times 5 - 4 \times 6, 2 \times 6 + 4 \times 5) = (10 - 24, 12 + 20) = (-14, 32)$. And

DEFINITION 3: $c \times (a, b) = (c \times a, c \times b)$.

For example, $3 \times (2, 4) = (3 \times 2, 3 \times 4) = (6, 12)$. This type of multiplication, called *scalar* multiplication, corresponds to a rule not given in the discussion of signed numbers and fractions: $a \times (c - d) = a \times c - a \times d$ and $a \times (c/d) = (a \times c)/d$; i.e., a rule for multiplying an integer by a positive integer and a fraction by an integer.

The definition of equality (compare $a + d = b + c$ for the equality of $a - b$ and $c - d$ and $a \times d = b \times c$ for the equality of a/b and c/d) is given by

DEFINITION 4: $(a, b) = (c, d)$ if $a = c$ and $b = d$.

For example, $(2, 3)$ is *not* equal to $(2, 1)$ for, while $2 = 2$, 3 is not equal to 1. Note that here we are defining what might be considered as logical identity. The pairs *cannot* look different and yet be equal, as is possible for integers and fractions. Hence we do not have to concern ourselves with the invariance question here.

---

[3] The reader may recall that I hesitated to use (a, b) for the signed numbers $a - b$ because, after all, the idea of a signed number and the use of the minus sign are generally known. Here I am assuming that most readers have not come across the usual $a + bi$ form of the complex numbers, and hence that they will have no prejudice against the (preferable) notation (a, b). Even if they have used the symbol (a, b) for the location of a point, the use here will not be too strange, since the vector interpretation given later ties in with this.

It is Definitions 2 and 3 which give a pair that behaves like the complex unit i. For if $b = d = 1$, $a = c = 0$; $a \times c - b \times d = 0 \times 0 - 1 \times 1 = -1$ and $a \times d + b \times c = 0 \times 1 + 1 \times 0 = 0$; so that

$$(1) \qquad (0,\ 1) \times (0,\ 1) = (-1,\ 0) = -1 \times (1,\ 0).$$

Thus if the complex number $(a, 0)$ is thought of as representing the real number a (cf. $(a + b) - b = a$ in Chapter 5 and $a/1 = a$ in Chapter 6) and $(0, 1)$ as representing the complex number i, the statement given in (1) is equivalent to the statement $i \times i = -1$. Of course, in letting $(a, 0)$ represent a, it must be checked that $(a, 0)$ behaves like a with respect to addition and multiplication. That is, it is observed, by Definition 1, that $(a, 0) + (c, 0) = (a + c, 0)$ and, by Definition 2, $(a, 0) \times (c, 0) = (a \times c, 0)$.

Continuing, the mathematician wants to show that these couples behave properly. The definition of proper behavior, as usual, is operation according to the assumptions laid down in Chapter 3 for the positive integers. Thus he has a series of theorems to prove as

THEOREM 7: $(a, b) + (c, d) = (c, d) + (a, b)$, the commutative law for addition.

Proof:

STEP	REASON
1. $(a, b) + (c, d) = (a + c, b + d)$	Definition 1
2. $(c, d) + (a, b) = (c + a, d + b)$	Definition 1
3. But $(a + c, b + d) = (c + a, d + b)$	Assumption 3, applied twice [4]

Similarly, the other assumptions of Chapter 3 (the associative laws, the commutative law for multiplication, and the distributive law) and Theorems 3 to 5 of Chapter 4 may be

---

[4] Since a, b, c, and d are allowed to be any real numbers, a law is being applied which has not been proved—i.e., the law that, under the assumptions for the positive integers, the commutative law for addition can be proved for all real numbers. This *can* be proved. But note that the underlying assumption *is* that made in Chapter 3.

proved to hold for complex numbers. Such details, however, are not necessary for our purposes.

I promised, however, to give a concrete realization of the complex numbers. To do this I make correspond to each complex number (i.e., to each pair of real numbers) a point in the plane according to the usual algebraic procedure— which should be clear from the figure below. Then, by (a, b)

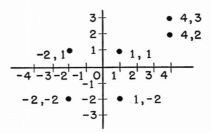

is meant the line (vector) drawn from O to the point corresponding to (a, b) as illustrated in the figure below. Then it

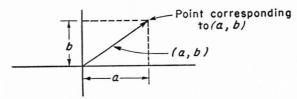

turns out that $(a, b) + (c, d)$ may be interpreted as the (by now familiar) vector obtained as the diagonal of the parallelogram, as shown below.

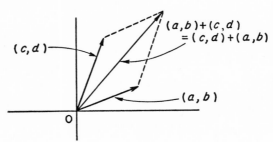

Unfortunately, however, the product of two complex numbers is not interpretable as the cross-product of two vectors discussed in Chapter 3. However, since $(1, 0) \times (0, 1) = (0, 1)$ (i.e., $1 \times i = i$), one can think of multiplication by $(0, 1)$ (i.e., i), as rotating the "unit" vector $(1, 0)$ through 90°.

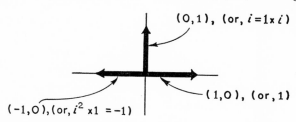

$(0,1)$, (or, $i = 1 \times i$)

$(1,0)$, (or, 1)

$(-1,0)$, (or, $i^2 \times 1 = -1$)

From this observation there is a good case for the statement that $(1, 0) \times (0, 1) \times (0, 1) = (-1, 0)$ (i.e., $1 \times i \times i = i^2 = -1$), since the vector $(-1, 0)$ is the vector $(1, 0)$ rotated through $180° = 2 \times 90°$. No pretense is made that this is a complete geometric treatment of the subject of complex numbers, but the details require a knowledge of trigonometry —and may be found in any book on that subject. One of the by-products of this treatment, by the way, is the rather amazing process of finding the square (and other) roots of complex numbers by what is called *De Moivre's theorem*. For example, one of the square roots of the complex number $(0, 1)$, (i.e., i), turns out to be $(\sqrt{2}/2, \sqrt{2}/2)$. That is, $(\sqrt{2}/2, \sqrt{2}/2) \times (\sqrt{2}/2, \sqrt{2}/2) = (0, 1)$—a fact that the reader may check by reference to Definition 2. Another interpretation of complex numbers will be made when *matrices* are discussed in Chapter 9.

It was mentioned in Chapter 5 that Cardan, while not completely sold on negative roots, nevertheless took the next bold step of dabbling to some extent with complex roots. However, he was far from accepting complex numbers in the general fashion that mathematicians do today, and his name is more frequently associated with "his" solution of the general cubic equation.[5] Now *his* must be put in quotation marks because it is known that Cardan obtained, and later published, the solution from a mathematician named Tartaglia after repeated requests and the most solemn promises of secrecy!

In order to understand this act of Cardan's, one needs to recall the whole atmosphere of Renaissance days in Italy. At that time the latest developments in both art and science were eagerly and passionately followed by the educated layman; and, to a much greater extent than is true today, the scientist depended on a popular reputation for advancement. And just as athletes, today, strive to maintain their popularity and reputation by contests with others, so, believe it or not, mathematicians held public contests in Renaissance Italy.

Frequently these contests dealt with the solution of cubic equations. Obviously, a man in possession of a method which would solve *all* cubics was in the position of a contemporary ball player who has learned how to hit all pitches! In such a position was our badly used friend, Tartaglia. Tartaglia's real name was Nicolo Fontana [6] (1499?–1557). When a boy of six, he was so badly cut up by a French soldier that he never again gained the free use of his tongue and hence was called *Tartaglia* (the stammerer). In addition to this, Tartaglia had the pressure of poverty to overcome. He did surmount this dual handicap and became one of the leading mathematicians of his time—only to have his name almost forgotten while that of his dastardly rival became immortalized.[7]

---

[5] Just as the general quadratic equation $ax^2 + bx + c = 0$, has a solution (formula), $x = (-b \pm \sqrt{b^2 - 4ac})/2a$, so does the general cubic, $ax^3 + bx^2 + cx + d = 0$ have a solution (more complicated, however).

[6] Another comparison with present-day adulation of sport heroes. How many know, for example, the real name of Babe Ruth?

[7] Perhaps some small retribution is made here. For Cardan is the more important man from our point of view—but most of my remarks are about Tartaglia!

The relation between complex numbers and vectors was first given by the Norwegian surveyor Casper Wessel in 1797, and independently, later, by the Swiss Jean Robert Argand in 1806. The writings of these men were little noticed, however, and it was not until Gauss (see below) took up the cudgels in behalf of complex numbers that they were fully accepted into the number family by all mathematicians.

It is worth noting that one of the major obstacles impeding the acceptance of these new numbers was their early label of "imaginary".[8] Fortunately, this word is being gradually eliminated, although it is still enough used to form a very real psychological barrier to the acceptance of these new numbers by many beginning students. This was recognized very early by Gauss, who wrote:

That this subject [complex numbers] has hitherto been considered from the wrong point of view and surrounded by a mysterious obscurity is to be attributed largely to an ill-adapted notation. If, for instance, $+1$, -1, $\sqrt{-1}$ [i] had been called direct, inverse, and lateral units instead of positive, negative, and imaginary (or even impossible), such an obscurity would have been out of the question.

Since *i* has been made a respectable member of our number family by various and sundry ingenious devices, the question now is: How many more curious characters will mathematicians need before they are able to solve all algebraic equations? Before this question is answered, let me recapitulate the work to date.

First of all, the objectives of this book may be stated again as follows: (1) To portray the development of a single line of mathematical thought from its most primitive beginnings to contemporary times, and (2) to make the abstractions of advanced mathematics easier to grasp by pointing out that the concreteness of elementary mathematics is largely illu-

---

[8] Just as negative numbers were once labeled as "fictitious" and "less than nothing".

sory and that, actually, all basic mathematics is abstract. The particular line of procedure employed (many others are possible) is that of the development of the number concept.

In carrying out this program, considerable time was first spent in exploring the most elementary idea of a positive integer—which is the technical nomenclature for the abstraction underlying the familiar whole numbers. Many thousands of years, it was noted, were necessary for developing the smooth notation and the simple rules which enable any sixth-grader to do quite complicated problems with whole numbers. Basically, however, the fact remains that the integers are abstractions, with rules and operations that are assumed rather than proved. Only the fact that the abstractions find so many realizations in everyday life causes them to be taken for concrete objects.

The signed numbers, zero, fractions, irrational numbers, and complex numbers were then successively introduced. Each of these was related to (that is, defined in terms of) the positive integers, and it was then stated (and even occasionally proved!) that the properties of these new numbers with respect to their (defined) addition and multiplication were identical with the properties originally assumed in Chapter 3 for the positive integers.

After the introduction of the positive integers, extensions of the number system to include zero, negative, irrational, and complex numbers were motivated by imagining attempts to solve more and more general equations. Although the process was not described, it was pointed out that fractions, too, could have been imagined as arising in this way, as, for example, $\frac{2}{3}$ from the equation $3x = 2$. The number -1 was considered as arising from the equation $x + 3 = 2$, 0 from the equation $x + b = b$, $\sqrt{2}$ from the equation $x^2 - 2 = 0$, and i from the equation $x^2 + 1 = 0$. Actually, as noted before, this unification idea is neither completely accurate, historically, nor is it the only way known today. However, it has, I hope, served a useful purpose, and I discard it now with regret.

But with regret or not, it must be dropped. For Karl Friedrich Gauss, the "Prince of Mathematicians", proved that no further generalizations of the number concept can arise out of the study of the solution of ordinary algebraic equations, even when the coefficients of such equations run wildly among any of the numbers previously mentioned. Thus, by his result, mathematicians know that the equation

$$ix^5 - \sqrt{3}\,x^4 + \sqrt[3]{1 + \sqrt{5}}\,x^3 + (1071/972)\,x^2 - \sqrt[5]{17/5}\,x + 1 = 0,$$

difficult as it might be to solve, has roots (five of them!) which are complex numbers [including real numbers as a special case, $b = 0$, of the complex numbers (a, b)].

Where, then, do we get the further generalizations that have kept, are keeping, and will continue to keep algebraists very busy?

In order to reach an answer to this question, there are two logical avenues of approach. One is to stop here and analyze in a more complete fashion the properties of the number systems displayed to this point, and then ask if there are other kinds of "numbers" which have similar properties. Such a line of attack would lead, for example, into the study of *integral domains* and *fields*. Although this may be the more logical way to proceed, the technical obstacles to be surmounted before problems of contemporary research could be arrived at are quite staggering. The other way of proceeding is to *discard* some of the restrictive assumptions enumerated for the integers in Chapter 3 (first, the commutative law for multiplication and, secondly, the associative law for multiplication) and see if any new numbers (called hypercomplex numbers) can then be invented, whose definition can be made in terms of real numbers and which deliberately violate these assumptions. Such will be the procedure in the concluding chapters.

Noting that the reason for the change in our procedure is due to one K. F. Gauss, we may accept him as the principal figure of this chapter—albeit in a rather negative fashion. But Gauss deserves more than passing mention in any book concerned with the development of mathematics. The title, *Princeps Mathematicorum,* was not bestowed just by me but was given to Gauss by his contemporaries as a tribute to his great achievements in almost every field of mathematics.

A prince in intellectual achievements but not by blood, Gauss was the son of poor parents. He was born at Brunswick, Germany, on April 30, 1777, and at the incredibly early age of three showed his mathematical proclivities by correcting his father in a sum the latter obtained in making out the weekly pay roll for the laborers under his charge. A continued succession of amazing feats of mathematical ability brought him to his doctorate at the age of twenty-two, with a dissertation proving that complex numbers suffice for the solution of ordinary algebraic equations.[9] From this he went on to a deep study of the theory of numbers to produce his greatest single work, the *Disquestiones Arithmeticae.* Besides founding the study of "analytic" functions of a complex variable, he made outstanding contributions to astronomy, geodesy, electromagnetism, and the theory of least squares. Finally, by reference to brief notes in his diary, it seems clear that he is also entitled to priority in invention of many other aspects of mathematics commonly attributed to others—such as non-Euclidean geometry, quaternion algebras (see next chapter), and analysis situs.

Unlike most mathematicians, Gauss continued active participation in the development of mathematics until near the

---

[9] Not a precise statement of the result. (See Appendix.)

end of a long life. He died on February 23, 1855, in his seventy-eighth year. His achievements were summed up by Kronecker, who wrote: "Almost everything which the mathematics of our [nineteenth] century has brought forth in the way of original scientific ideas attaches to the name of Gauss."

PROBLEMS

1. Add $(1, 2)$ and $(3, 4)$.
2. Multiply $(1, 2)$ by $(3, 4)$.
3. Check that $(\sqrt{2}/2, \sqrt{2}/2)^2 = (0, 1)$.
4. Perform the scalar multiplication of $(3, 4)$ by 2.
5. Prove that $[(a, b) + (c, d)] + (e, f) = (a, b) + [(c, d) + (e, f)]$. What law is this?
6. By the use of vectors, give a geometric picture of the sum of $(-1, 1)$ and $(2, 3)$.

Chapter 9

A SHOT IN THE ARM FOR COMPLACENT ALGEBRAISTS OF THE NINETEENTH CENTURY

FROM Cardan's first use of complex numbers in 1545 to Gauss' doctoral dissertation of 1799 stretches a period of over two hundred and fifty years for which I have recorded no outstanding mathematical advances. Since there were many, though not in algebra, and since Gauss boldly foretold the shape of much of the modern mathematics which followed close after him, this seems like a good place to take a deep historical breath before considering the next big step.

This algebraically inactive period ranges from the middle of the sixteenth century to the end of the eighteenth, from the birth of Shakespeare to the time of Goethe, from the beginnings of the Reformation to the heyday of Deism, from Palestrina to Beethoven, from Copernicus' *De Revolutionibus Orbium Coelestium* to Laplace's *Exposition of the System of the World,* from alchemy to the overthrow of the phlogiston theory, from the early beginnings of observational biology to the classification system of Linnaeus. And in mathematics is recorded the development of analytic geometry by René Descartes (1596–1650), the great achievements of Pierre de Fermat (1601–1665) in number theory, and, overshadowing all, the invention of the calculus by Isaac Newton (1642–1727) and Gottfried von Leibnitz (1646–1716). Immediately following Newton and Leibnitz, the development of the calculus was the prime task confronting mathematicians. Of these, Leonhard Euler (1707–1783) was the most prominent.

96

Striding past Gauss, we now faintly hear his "I could have told you so" as the mathematical world greeted with mingled delight and alarm the non-Euclidean geometries of the Russian mathematician Nicolai Lobachevski in 1829 and the Hungarian mathematician Farkas Bolyai in 1833. For these Copernici of geometry showed mathematicians for the first time that axioms were not God-given self-evident truths and hence, as is clear from what has been said thus far, opened up a very important aspect of mathematics. In algebra the next important date is 1843. For this was the year in which Sir William Rowan Hamilton invented quaternions, and in so doing opened up a rich vein of algebraic treasures which has been worked with profit for over a century. And as will be described later, at about the time that the vein seemed to be losing some of its richness, a side pocket was opened up which brought new prospectors on the run.

Although Hamilton first conceived of his quaternions as the tool for the answer to a geometrical problem, it would take us too far afield to go into the details of this method of approach. Instead, imagine a mythical mathematician who has observed the success of the development of a new type of number (the complex numbers) by consideration of *pairs* of real numbers, and who asks whether or not this process can be extended to *triples, quadruples,* etc. of real numbers. He would expect, of course, that the properties of these new numbers would be the same as those of the complex numbers with respect to the laws of addition and multiplication (just as Hamilton did); and this would hinder him a good deal (as it did Hamilton) since, in a certain technical sense, it turns out that "higher" numbers can be developed only by sacrificing some of the laws of complex numbers. For the quaternions, which are *quadruples* of real numbers, it is the commutative law for multiplication that becomes the burnt offering to the gods of algebra. Of course, admittedly, our mythical mathematician should consider *triples* as the next logical step, but it so happens that to attain triples still another property of real and complex numbers must be sacrificed (namely, the fact that $a \times b = 0$ implies that a and/or b is zero—Theorem 4). Clearly this would be a little too shocking as a starter (although calmly accepted by any mathematician today). So without further ado, I shall proceed to describe what is essentially the closest approximation to the complex numbers which uses the technique of definition in terms of sets of real numbers.[1]

Consider, then, a set of quadruples of real numbers, (a, b, c, d). As in the case of complex numbers, $(a, b, c, d) = (e, f, g, h)$ if and only if $a = e, b = f, c = g, d = h$. Then, still following the pattern of the complex number development—with certain unpleasant lengthenings of the formulas—addition is defined by

(1) $(a, b, c, d) + (e, f, g, h) = (a+e, b+f, c+g, d+h)$

For example, $(1, 1, 2, 3) + (2, 1, 4, 2) = (1+2, 1+1, 2+4, 3+2) = (3, 2, 6, 5)$. This is simple enough. But multiplication is defined by

(2) $(a, b, c, d) \times (e, f, g, h) = (a \times e - b \times f - c \times g$
$- d \times h, a \times f + b \times e + c \times h - d \times g, a \times g + c \times e$
$+ d \times f - b \times h, a \times h + b \times g + d \times e - c \times f)$

For example, $(1, 1, 2, 3) \times (2, 1, 4, 2) = (1 \times 2 - 1 \times 1 - 2 \times 4 - 3 \times 2, 1 \times 1 + 1 \times 2 + 2 \times 2 - 3 \times 4, 1 \times 4 + 2 \times 2 + 3 \times 1 - 1 \times 2, 1 \times 2 + 1 \times 4 + 3 \times 2 - 2 \times 1) = (2 - 1 - 8 - 6, 1 + 2 + 4 - 12, 4 + 4 + 3 - 2, 2 + 4 + 6 - 2) = (-13, -5, 9, 10)$. Finally, scalar multiplication is defined by

(3) $e \times (a, b, c, d) = (e \times a, e \times b, e \times c, e \times d),$

---

[1] Technically, the algebraists say that the only division algebra of order four over the real numbers is the quaternions. A good deal of the difficulty in advanced mathematics is caused by the need to master a large and esoteric vocabulary.

For example, $5 \times (1, 1, 2, 3) = (5 \times 1, 5 \times 1, 5 \times 2, 5 \times 3) = (5, 5, 10, 15)$.

In order to grasp the significance of these involved formulas, first note that, if $b = c = d = f = g = h = 0$, we have, from (1),

$$(a, 0, 0, 0) + (e, 0, 0, 0) = (a + e, 0, 0, 0)$$

and, from (2),

$$(a, 0, 0, 0) \times (e, 0, 0, 0) = (a \times e, 0, 0, 0).$$

That is, these special quaternions, $(a, 0, 0, 0)$, behave just like the real numbers. Hence the quaternions may be regarded as a true generalization of real numbers, since they include, as special cases, quantities which behave like the real numbers. They may also be thought of as a true generalization of complex numbers, since, if we now take $c = d = g = h = 0$ we have, from (2),

$$(a, b, 0, 0,) \times (e, f, 0, 0) = (a \times e - b \times f, a \times f + b \times e, 0, 0)$$

which is essentially the formula for complex number multiplication given in Chapter 8. (It differs only in that c, d is replaced by e, f and that quadruples with two zeros are used in place of pairs.) Furthermore, just as $(0, 1)$ was called i in the complex number case, $(0, 1, 0, 0)$ is called i in the quaternions; $(0, 0, 1, 0)$, j; $(0, 0, 0, 1)$, k; and $(1, 0, 0, 0)$, 1. These quantities 1, i, j, and k are the quaternionic "units" which correspond to the complex "units", 1 and i. And just as the algebra of complex numbers is essentially determined by the behavior of 1 and i, so the behavior of the quaternions is essentially determined by the behavior of 1, i, j, and k.

Now how do 1, i, j, and k behave? To observe them, first take $a = c = d = e = g = h = 0$ and $b = f = 1$ in formula (2). Then (2) becomes

$$(0, 1, 0, 0,) \times (0, 1, 0, 0) = (-1, 0, 0, 0) = -1 \times (1, 0, 0, 0),$$

(i.e., $i^2 = -1$), as in complex numbers. But likewise, by the same procedure, it may be shown that $j^2 = k^2 = -1$. Does this mean that $i = j$ or k? No! For $i = j$ would mean that $(0, 1, 0, 0) = (0, 0, 1, 0)$, which is contrary to the definition of equality. Nor is $i = -j$ or $-k$. Clearly, such a situation would be impossible if i, j, and k were real or even complex numbers. But as they are quadruples of real numbers, the strangeness of the conclusions only matches the strangeness of the definition of the numbers.

The second surprise arises when $i \times j$ is computed by formula (2) and compared with $j \times i$. For $i \times j$ we have

$$(0, 1, 0, 0) \times (0, 0, 1, 0) = (0, 0, 0, 1),$$

(i.e., $i \times j = k$), while for $j \times i$ we have

$$(0, 0, 1, 0) \times (0, 1, 0, 0) = (0, 0, 0, -1) = -1 \times (0, 0, 0, 1),$$

(i.e., $j \times i = -k$; $i \times j = -j \times i$). It is to be hoped, however, that the surprise is not too great. For these quaternions are abstract quantities whose properties are not at all known to us. In particular, of course, they are not to be identified with a certain herd of cows or chairs in a room, as our integers commonly are (although, as pointed out, without real justification). Compare, however, the cross-product of vectors mentioned in Chapter 3 where it was shown that the product, $i \times j$, of the two vectors i and j was not the same as the product $j \times i$.

Surprises, however, are essentially at an end in the realm of quaternionic algebra. Except for the fact that there are six different quantities, $(i, -i, j, -j, k, -k)$, the square of each of which is -1 (instead of only two, $(i, -i)$, as in the algebra of complex numbers), and the fact that the commutative law for multiplication breaks down, the quaternions are well behaved. That is, they obey the other assumptions that were laid down for the positive integers in Chapter 3 and the Theorems 3 to 5 of Chapter 4. In addition, it may be shown that each quaternion has an inverse; i.e., for every quaternion X there is a quaternion Y such that $X \times Y = Y \times X$

$= 1 = (1, 0, 0, 0)$, just as in the case of the algebra of rational, real, or complex numbers.

Now consider the second system that illustrates the new types of numbers used by modern algebraists [2]—the so-called *total* (or *full*) *matric* algebra of *order* four. Here, however, while it is possible to continue to use the device of a quadruple of real numbers (with, of course, a different rule for multiplication—but the same for addition), it is more convenient not to do so. Also, by using a new device for exhibiting these numbers, the reader will be introduced to a side topic of algebra which is of considerable practical importance. This will be the concept of a *matrix*, introduced in 1858 by Arthur Cayley.

A matrix (not to be confused with the determinant of college algebra) may be thought of as arising from the study of linear equations (or, more precisely, linear transformations). Thus if there are four quantities designated by t, u, x, and y that are related to each other by means of the (linear) equations

$$(4) \qquad \begin{aligned} t &= 2x + 3y \\ u &= x + 4y, \end{aligned}$$

it is apparent that the essential things about this algebraic statement are not the letters x and y (which, after all, might have been called a and b) but the coefficients 2, 3, 1, and 4 and the order in which they appear. It is with this thought in mind that the square array

$$\begin{pmatrix} 2 & 3 \\ 1 & 4 \end{pmatrix},$$

called a matrix of order two, is formed. In order to call such quantities generalized (i.e., hypercomplex) numbers, equality of two matrices must be defined and instructions given to add and multiply two matrices. The definitions of equality

---

[2] As well as other mathematicians, statisticians, physicists, engineers, psychologists, and others.

and addition are very similar to the corresponding definitions for the quaternions. Thus

$$\begin{pmatrix} a & b \\ c & d \end{pmatrix} = \begin{pmatrix} e & f \\ g & h \end{pmatrix}$$

if and only if $a = e$, $b = f$, $c = g$, and $d = h$, and

$$\begin{pmatrix} a & b \\ c & d \end{pmatrix} + \begin{pmatrix} e & f \\ g & h \end{pmatrix} = \begin{pmatrix} a+e & b+f \\ c+g & d+h \end{pmatrix}.$$

For example,

$$\begin{pmatrix} 2 & 3 \\ 1 & 4 \end{pmatrix} + \begin{pmatrix} 2 & 5 \\ 6 & 5 \end{pmatrix} = \begin{pmatrix} 2+2 & 3+5 \\ 1+6 & 4+5 \end{pmatrix} = \begin{pmatrix} 4 & 8 \\ 7 & 9 \end{pmatrix}.$$

For scalar multiplication:

$$e \times \begin{pmatrix} a & b \\ c & d \end{pmatrix} = \begin{pmatrix} e \times a & e \times b \\ e \times c & e \times d \end{pmatrix}.$$

The formula for multiplication is more complicated (as was the case in the quaternion algebra), but there is an easy way to remember it, which I shall describe later. An excellent motivation for this definition of multiplication can also be provided if the question of two successive transformations of the form given in (4) were to be considered. However, since the details involve somewhat more formal algebra than I care to use in the text, they are relegated to the Appendix. Multiplication, then, is defined by

$$(5) \begin{pmatrix} a & b \\ c & d \end{pmatrix} \times \begin{pmatrix} e & f \\ g & h \end{pmatrix} = \begin{pmatrix} a \times e + b \times g & a \times f + b \times h \\ c \times e + d \times g & c \times f + d \times h \end{pmatrix}.$$

In order to remember this rule for what is called "row by column" multiplication, call the pair of numbers, (a, b), the first *row* of the first matrix; (c, d), the second row of the first matrix; (e, f), the first row of the second matrix; $\begin{pmatrix} a \\ c \end{pmatrix}$, the first *column* of the first matrix; $\begin{pmatrix} f \\ h \end{pmatrix}$, the second column of the second matrix, etc.

Now look again at formula (5): The element $a \times e + b \times g$ is in the first row and the first column of the product matrix and is thus to be obtained by taking the first row of the first matrix *into* the first column of the second matrix, as is indicated diagrammatically below.

$$(a, b) \begin{pmatrix} e \\ g \end{pmatrix} \quad \text{or} \quad \begin{matrix} a \times e \\ + \\ b \times g \end{matrix}$$

Similarly, the element $a \times f + b \times h$ is in the first row and second column of the product, and so is obtained by taking the first row of the first matrix into the second column of the second matrix, as shown by

$$(a, b) \begin{pmatrix} f \\ h \end{pmatrix} \quad \text{or} \quad \begin{matrix} a \times f \\ + \\ b \times h \end{matrix} \text{, etc.}$$

For example,

$$\begin{pmatrix} 2 & 3 \\ 1 & 4 \end{pmatrix} \times \begin{pmatrix} 2 & 5 \\ -1 & -5 \end{pmatrix} = \begin{pmatrix} 1 & -5 \\ -2 & -15 \end{pmatrix}$$

because

$$(2, 3) \begin{pmatrix} 2 \\ -1 \end{pmatrix} = 2 \times 2 + 3 \times (-1) = 4 + (-3) = 1,$$

$$(2, 3) \begin{pmatrix} 5 \\ -5 \end{pmatrix} = 2 \times 5 + 3 \times (-5) = 10 + (-15) = -5,$$

$$(1, 4) \begin{pmatrix} 2 \\ -1 \end{pmatrix} = 2 \times 1 + 4 \times (-1) = 2 + (-4) = -2,$$

$$(1, 4) \begin{pmatrix} 5 \\ -5 \end{pmatrix} = 1 \times 5 + 4 \times (-5) = 5 + (-20) = -15.$$

The set of *all* two by two matrices under the definitions of equality, addition, and multiplication, just made, is what is called the total (or full) matric algebra of order four; and it possesses many peculiar properties. First, these new "numbers" are not generally commutative with respect to multiplication. For example,

$$\begin{pmatrix} 2 & 3 \\ 1 & 4 \end{pmatrix} \times \begin{pmatrix} 2 & 5 \\ -1 & -5 \end{pmatrix} = \begin{pmatrix} 1 & -5 \\ -2 & -15 \end{pmatrix}$$

while

$$\begin{pmatrix} 2 & 5 \\ -1 & -5 \end{pmatrix} \times \begin{pmatrix} 2 & 3 \\ 1 & 4 \end{pmatrix} = \begin{pmatrix} 9 & 26 \\ -7 & -23 \end{pmatrix}.$$

Furthermore, while it is true that for all the number systems hitherto described (including the quaternions), $a \times b = 0$ implies that a and/or b is zero (Theorem 4), it is not true here if by zero is meant, naturally, the matrix $\begin{pmatrix} 0 & 0 \\ 0 & 0 \end{pmatrix}$. For

$$\begin{pmatrix} 1 & 0 \\ 0 & 0 \end{pmatrix} \neq \begin{pmatrix} 0 & 0 \\ 0 & 0 \end{pmatrix}, \begin{pmatrix} 0 & 0 \\ 0 & 1 \end{pmatrix} \neq \begin{pmatrix} 0 & 0 \\ 0 & 0 \end{pmatrix},$$

but

$$\begin{pmatrix} 1 & 0 \\ 0 & 0 \end{pmatrix} \times \begin{pmatrix} 0 & 0 \\ 0 & 1 \end{pmatrix} = \begin{pmatrix} 0 & 0 \\ 0 & 0 \end{pmatrix}.$$

Many other curious properties of these new numbers could be given, but the ones set forth above should convince the reader of their dissimilarity to ordinary numbers. On the other hand, matrices do retain many of the important properties that were originally attributed to positive integers, such as the commutative and associative laws for addition, the associative law for multiplication, and the distributive law for multiplication with respect to addition.

In fact, the matrix $\begin{pmatrix} 1 & 0 \\ 0 & 1 \end{pmatrix}$ acts like "1", i.e.,

$$\begin{pmatrix} 1 & 0 \\ 0 & 1 \end{pmatrix} \times \begin{pmatrix} a & b \\ c & d \end{pmatrix} = \begin{pmatrix} a & b \\ c & d \end{pmatrix} \times \begin{pmatrix} 1 & 0 \\ 0 & 1 \end{pmatrix} = \begin{pmatrix} a & b \\ c & d \end{pmatrix}.$$

Furthermore,

$$(6) \quad \begin{pmatrix} 0 & 1 \\ -1 & 0 \end{pmatrix} \times \begin{pmatrix} 0 & 1 \\ -1 & 0 \end{pmatrix} = \begin{pmatrix} -1 & 0 \\ 0 & -1 \end{pmatrix} = (-1) \times \begin{pmatrix} 1 & 0 \\ 0 & 1 \end{pmatrix},$$

so that another "realization" of the complex number i is obtained (as promised in Chapter 8). That is, by (6), the matrix $\begin{pmatrix} 0 & 1 \\ -1 & 0 \end{pmatrix}$ behaves like i, in that its square is the negative of the unit matrix, just as the square of i is the negative of the unit 1. In general, the complex number (a, b) (or $a + bi$) is represented by the matrix $\begin{pmatrix} a & b \\ -b & a \end{pmatrix}$.

A word in conclusion about the uses of these new numbers. The quaternions led to the development of the intensely practical vector analysis which the physicist uses so extensively. And matrices are used in such diverse connections as statistical analysis, the solution of differential equations that arise in aircraft design, the factor analysis of the psychologist, the wave mechanics of the atomic physicist, and a type of cryptogram.[3] Matric algebras (as contrasted with the individual matrices), however, are mainly important as key elements in the structural analysis of more general types of algebras that will be discussed in the next chapter.

The originators of the subject matter of this chapter are two men with personalities worlds apart: the exuberant

---

[3] In the last-named application, they are used in combination with a set of integers modulo a prime number—such as is described in Chapter 4.

Irishman Sir William Rowan Hamilton and the phlegmatic Englishman Arthur Cayley. The senior member of the duo is Hamilton—by some sixteen years—so he will be considered first.

Our Irish tragedy (as E. T. Bell calls it in his *Men of Mathematics*) opens on August 3, 1805, with our hero off to a rapid start in his astonishing career by learning to be an accomplished reader of English by three; of Latin, Greek, and Hebrew by five; Italian and French by eight; Arabic and Sanskrit by ten; and—or shall I conclude by simply stating that Hamilton realized that there was no real point in all this by the time he was fourteen (and had just mastered Persian)? Anyway, such an intense concentration on languages should make us tolerant of the fact that, with a late beginning, Hamilton did not master the calculus until he was seventeen and did not make any monumental discovery in mathematics until he was almost eighteen!

But stop! By now the reader (if he has managed to swallow all of the above about Hamilton) must be convinced that the lad must have been an insufferable prig. Far from it. As a boy he had a normal interest in sports; had a serious love affair at nineteen, and, unfortunately, was not at all averse to a drop of Irish dew from time to time.

To go on. Although Hamilton never attended any school before going to the university, in 1823 he passed first out of one hundred candidates into Trinity College, Dublin. The reader may well imagine the series of triumphs, prizes, and honors awaiting him there—culminating in the incredible climax when young Hamilton, an undergraduate of twenty-two, was unanimously elected by the governing board of Trinity to a professorship of astronomy. No great discoveries in astronomy proper were made by the fledgling professor, but a year later he completed work on some investigations that he had begun at eighteen and published Part I of his *A Theory of Systems of Rays*—one of the classics of optics.

Since our real interest here is in his later invention of quaternions, let us leave this scene of great achievement and consider briefly the two major evil influences that took their toll of his genius: marriage and alcohol. Hamilton's first major love affair at nineteen has already been mentioned. After a second one, Hamilton married, in his twenty-eighth year, Helen Maria Bayley. No high tragedy here. Just an ordinary tale of a (psychologically?) ailing female who let her servants turn their household—especially her husband's study—into a reasonably close facsimile of a pigsty.

Partly as a result of his domestic difficulties, and partly as a result of being a brilliant and jolly young man much in demand for parties and dinners, Hamilton made his predicament more sordid by excessive drinking. He did pull himself short on this for a brief period after about ten years of marriage, but slid back again two years later. Not, of course, into anything resembling the condition of a denizen of skid row. For at thirty he was knighted, at thirty-two he became president of the Royal Irish Academy, and at thirty-eight the British government awarded him a Civil List life pension of two hundred pounds a year.

It was shortly before this last honor came to him that Hamilton introduced quaternions to the world by carving the fundamental formulas of his new algebra on the stone of the bridge he was standing on when the great idea of abandoning commutativity came to him.

As an opening gun in the all-out attack of later mathematicians on the axioms of ordinary algebra, quaternions cannot be too highly regarded. As a system in themselves, however, they are, while important, not tremendously so. But it was Hamilton's fate to add an obsession for quaternions to his obsession for drink. As a result, the last twenty years of his life were devoted almost entirely to the development and applications of quaternions—work which is of little significance today.

And so till the end with his death from gout on September 2, 1865. His name lives today in the "Hamiltonian" principles of physics which find their inspiration in his early work on optics. As for quaternions—today we have the generalized quaternions of L. E. Dickson and the generalization of A. A. Albert of the generalized Dickson quaternions, all of which would have delighted Hamilton more than a dozen Hamiltonian principles!

Like Hamilton, Arthur Cayley, born August 16, 1821 at Richmond, Surrey, showed his mathematical proclivities early in life and also entered Trinity College (but at Cambridge!) at eighteen. Quickly achieving first place in mathematics, he became a Fellow of Trinity and assistant tutor, publishing his first mathematical work when he was twenty. While lacking the extreme versatility of Hamilton, Cayley too was a man with interests other than mathematics. His proficiency in languages, while offering no competition to Hamilton's, included a good knowledge of Greek, French, German, and Italian. He was an avid reader of the fiction of the time, with Sir Walter Scott and Jane Austen as his favorite authors. In the line of physical activity, mountain climbing ranked high with him, and he greatly enjoyed this sport on his trips to Switzerland—along with a deep appreciation of the fine arts in adjacent Northern Italy.

Furthermore, after leaving Cambridge in 1846, Cayley began training for the bar and was admitted three years later. There he made a modest reputation for himself as well as a comfortable livelihood. But his real love was still mathematics, and during his years of bondage to the law he published over two hundred mathematical papers—some of which are now classics. Finally, in 1863, Cambridge University found a post for Cayley; and in the same year Cayley married Susan Moline.

In 1858 he introduced the concept of a matrix. This idea grew out of his abiding interest in "invariants" and served originally only as a tool in those investigations. However, as has often happened, the tool became a theory of importance in its own right. Today, in fact, the ideas of matrix theory are more important than those of much of the classical invariant theory (although the basic concept of "invariance" is still of fundamental importance).

One more accomplishment of Cayley's should be mentioned here—and a very curious one it is. For Cayley was a contemporary of Hamilton's and hence lived at a time when mathematicians were just beginning to be emancipated from the commutative law for multiplication. It was to be many years before a similar emancipation movement in regard to the associative law received popular support. (See Chapter 12.) But Cayley did take this next step, in 1843, in connection with his sketch of a geometry of n-dimensions. For just as Hamilton found it necessary to abandon the commutative law in his search for an algebra to apply to three-dimensional geometry,[4] Cayley also ran into the necessity for abandoning the associative law in the four-dimensional[5] case.

Liked by all who knew him, and respected as much for his character as for his mathematical genius, Cayley bore a long and painful illness with resignation and fortitude and died on January 26, 1895. His name is immortalized in the "Cayley" algebras, of which more will be said later.

To complete the historical picture of the early genesis of modern algebras, recall that as early as 1819 K. F. Gauss wrote out, but never published, an outline of the theory of quaternions (which he called "mutations in space"). Likewise, in 1844, H. G. Grassmann (1809–1877) not only presented a theory of what were potentially quaternions, but he

---

[4] Recall that the mathematician who conceived quaternions as generalizations of the complex numbers by the 4-tuple device was purely mythical!

[5] This is not the four dimensions of the metaphysicians, but a purely mathematical—i.e., abstract—idea.

also sketched out a line of generalization which was later taken up and developed by others. (See the next chapter.) Unfortunately, his book (*Ausdehnungslehre*) abounds in philosophical verbosity which repelled the mathematician from it so that, as a result, Grassmann was not to receive full credit for his penetrating insight until much later.

PROBLEMS

1. Add $(0, 1, 1, 1)$ and $(1, 0, 2, 3)$.
2. Multiply $(0, 1, 1, 1)$ by $(1, 0, 2, 3)$.
3. Add $\begin{pmatrix} 0 & 1 \\ 3 & 2 \end{pmatrix}$ and $\begin{pmatrix} 1 & 0 \\ 1 & 4 \end{pmatrix}$.
4. Multiply $\begin{pmatrix} 0 & 1 \\ 3 & 2 \end{pmatrix}$ by $\begin{pmatrix} 1 & 0 \\ 1 & 4 \end{pmatrix}$

Chapter 10

HOW LASTING WAS THE SHOT?

I T is all very well to describe some of the systems invented by algebraists, but as a matter of fact, it takes no great skill to invent any number of such systems, once bold men have helped achieve emancipation from some of the restrictive laws of algebra.[1] The real points that still need to be considered here are: what may be done with these systems (mathematically—not in the sense of physical application), and in what sense are the two examples given in Chapter 9 typical?

As to the first question. One may try to develop relations and procedures in these systems similar to those used in the algebra of complex numbers. For example, for the quaternions, mathematicians have worked out a theory of solutions of equations involving quaternions as coefficients, similar to that for equations involving only complex numbers as coefficients. (This is actually a relatively minor task, but the explanation of deeper problems would involve an excess of technical terms.)

And perhaps it would be well at this point to emphasize again how narrow a mathematical path we are treading. First of all, we made a choice of beginning with the positive integers, whereas many other systems could have been chosen as starters. Secondly, we considered only one set of assumptions characterizing the positive integers, whereas,

---

[1] That is, an idea is easy or not easy, only relative to the time in history and the amount of background or formal training. Thus today's commonplace of "zero" took a lot of thought centuries ago. Furthermore, although the reader should find himself in general agreement with the view expressed, he may lack the mathematical background to do any actual construction himself.

again, there are others. Then after the topics normally included in freshman and sophomore algebra had been discussed [2] (i.e., through complex numbers), I chose to continue
our discussion with a treatment of linear algebra rather than
algebraic numbers, groups, rings, fields, or others of the many
types of mathematical systems. Finally, in the realm of linear
algebra itself, we are ignoring, for example, the important
problem of the "arithmetic" of algebras. Part of the choices
made is arbitrary, part is due to my personal prejudice in
favor of certain topics, but I believe most of the choices are
dictated by my announced intention of portraying a single
line of mathematical thought from its most primitive beginnings to modern times.

In any case, at this point we are going to consider the important problem of investigating what is called the *structure
theory* of hypercomplex systems (or, as they are commonly
called today, linear algebras). A crude analogy to this problem can be made by considering the decomposition of integers into products of primes. For example, $6 = 2 \times 3$
where 2 and 3 have no factors except themselves and unity.
Since all integers can be so decomposed, at least some of the
properties of the integers can be obtained from a knowledge
of the properties of primes. Likewise, physicists study the
"prime" particles—the electron, proton, *et al.*—and how they
combine to give all elements. Thus, here, the first question
is, what are the "prime" algebras.

Before they are described, however, some attempt at a
precise definition of a (linear associative) algebra (over the
real field [3]) should be made. There are three rather different

---

[2] In a way, however, quite different from that used in most undergraduate algebra courses.

[3] The phrase "over the real field" (which will be omitted from now on)
means that in the couples, triples, quadruples, etc., real numbers will be
used. That is, in (a, b), (a, b, c, d), $\cdots$, a, b, c, d, are real numbers. In
general, the mathematician uses the elements of any *field*—a field being a
generalization of the real number system.

ways in which a definition may be formulated, and all three ways have been at least partially illustrated. The first is by way of the couple device, extended, as for the quaternions, to 4-tuples and in general to n-tuples. The second approach is by use of "units" such as 1, i for the complex numbers and 1, i, j, k for the quaternions. The third, and most modern (1951) way, is to impose upon these n-tuples what are called linear transformations which in turn may be represented by matrices. From this point of view, the total matric algebra of the previous chapter is looked upon as the set of all linear transformations on what is called a linear (or vector) space of dimension two.

None of the precise definitions can be stated very simply, but here is a rough version of one in terms of n-tuples as follows.

(The reader is invited to skip this!)

DEFINITION: A linear associative algebra A is a set of n-tuples $(a_1, a_2, \cdots, a_n)$ where $a_1, a_2, \cdots, a_n$ are real numbers, where equality is determined by the statement that

$$(a_1, a_2, \cdots, a_n) = (b_1, b_2, \cdots, b_n)$$

if and only if $a_1 = b_1$, $a_2 = b_2$, $\cdots$, $a_n = b_n$; addition by

$$(a_1, a_2, \cdots, a_n) + (b_1, b_2, \cdots, b_n)$$
$$= (a_1 + b_1, a_2 + b_2, \cdots, a_n + b_n);$$

scalar multiplication by

$$c \times (a_1, a_2, \cdots, a_n) = (c \times a_1, c \times a_2, \cdots, c \times a_n)$$

and multiplication by (as usual, this is the tough one)

$$(a_1, a_2, \cdots, a_n) \times (b_1, b_2, \cdots, b_n) = (c_1, c_2, \cdots, c_n)$$

where the c's are combinations of the a's and b's as follows:

$$c_1 = d_{11}^{(1)} a_1 b_1 + d_{12}^{(1)} a_1 b_2 + \cdots + d_{1n}^{(1)} a_1 b_n + d_{21}^{(1)} a_2 b_1 + \cdots$$
$$\cdots + d_{nn}^{(1)} a_n b_n,$$

$$c_2 = d_{11}^{(2)} a_1 b_1 + d_{12}^{(2)} a_1 b_2 + \cdots + d_{1n}^{(2)} a_1 b_n + d_{21}^{(2)} a_2 b_1 + \cdots$$
$$\cdots + d_{nn}^{(2)} a_n b_n,$$

$$\cdot \quad \cdot \quad \cdot \quad \cdot \quad \cdot \quad \cdot \quad \cdot \quad \cdot \quad \cdot \quad \cdot \quad \cdot \quad \cdot \quad \cdot \quad \cdot \quad \cdot \quad \cdot \quad \cdot \quad \cdot \quad \cdot$$

$$c_n = d_{11}^{(n)} a_1 b_1 + d_{12}^{(n)} a_1 b_2 + \cdots + d_{1n}^{(n)} a_1 b_n + d_{21}^{(n)} a_2 b_1 + \cdots$$
$$\cdots + d_{nn}^{(n)} a_n b_n,$$

(all a's, b's, c's, and d's real numbers)[4]; and where, finally, we demand that the multiplication be associative (this puts certain conditions on the d's).

In the search for the "prime" components of an arbitrary algebra, three distinct types are found: the *division* algebras, the *total matric* algebras, and the *nilpotent* algebras. Two examples of a division algebra have already been given—the complex numbers and the quaternions. These algebras are characterized by the property of having inverses or, by what amounts to the same thing, the property that $a \times b = 0$ implies that a or b is zero. As for total matric algebras, an example is the total matric algebra of order four—and the ones of higher order are formed similarily (as all matrices of order three give rise to a total matric algebra of order nine).

There is no real need to define or even give an example of a nilpotent algebra. It suffices simply to say that it is a type of algebra quite distinct from either a division algebra or a total matric algebra. (See problem at end of chapter.) Having described these fundamental types of algebras with the utmost brevity, this rapid sketch of the structure theory of algebras is completed by stating that, by *appropriate* combinations of these types, all possible algebras may be constructed. Note that the weak analogy to the decomposition of integers into the product of primes broke down when

---

[4] The only reason for inflicting the sight of this on the reader is that to me it doesn't seem quite right to talk about general algebras without some attempt at a general definition. However, so far as the remaining discussion goes, any other definition would do about as well!

it was found that there were three "types" of "primes" (division, total matric, and nilpotent). Further weakening takes place now, in that to break down an arbitrary algebra, three different types of decomposition must be used—a *sum*, a *direct sum*, and a *direct product*. Each of these terms just mentioned is, of course, a highly technical one; and it would require considerable effort and background on the part of the reader to master their meaning. Fortunately, it is not the meaning of the terms but the underlying method of attack which is important. This method can be summarized as follows:

Any algebra A is the *sum* of a so-called *semi-simple* algebra B and a *nilpotent* algebra N, i.e.,

$$A = B + N.$$

Then, in turn, B is the *direct sum* of so-called *simple* algebras, $E_1, E_2, \cdots, E_n$, i.e.,

$$B = E_1 \oplus E_2 \oplus \cdots \oplus E_n,$$

where a circle is used around the plus sign to distinguish this type of addition from the one used before. Finally, each simple algebra is the *direct product* of a *total matric* algebra and a *division* algebra, i.e.,

$$E_1 = M_1 \times D_1, E_2 = M_2 \times D_2, \cdots, E_n = M_n \times D_n,$$

so that, by analyzing the M's, the D's, N, $+$, $\oplus$, and $\times$, the algebraist analyzes A.

If we leave out most of the technical words, the above may be rewritten as:

Any algebra A is a type 1 sum of a b-type algebra and an n-type algebra. In turn, a b-type algebra is a type 2 sum of s-type algebras. Finally, s-type algebras are products of m-type algebras and d-type algebras. Hence algebraists need study only m-type, d-type, and n-type algebras, together with their three methods of combination.

This last expression of procedure is just as meaningful as the first and with a few changes could be made to apply to the analysis of groups, rings, and other objects of current mathematical study.

There are, however, two big problems still on hand (as well as a host of other problems) on which mathematicians are currently (1951) working. One is concerned with a lack of preciseness in the description of one of the three types of "linkages" (the *sum*) that is used to get all possible types of algebras from the basic three. So long as this point remains unsettled, it is clear that the theory cannot be regarded as complete, since the statement that all algebras can be generated from the basic three is not meaningful unless a detailed description of the process of formation is known. The other big problem is concerned with the analysis of one of the basic types—the nilpotent algebras. Here, too, it is clear that the statement that all algebras can be generated from the basic three is not meaningful unless the structure of the three types is completely known. Although the total matric algebras are quite simple to analyze, and division algebras have been thoroughly analyzed over special fields at least (see below for comment on division algebras over the real number field), very little is known about nilpotent algebras.

The reader may very well object that there is too much vagueness in this chapter. But this seems unavoidable unless he is willing to master a considerable amount of technical jargon (such as *ideal, sum, direct sum,* and *direct product*) and to work through the details of some examples, as is done in my article in the *American Mathematical Monthly* [5] (written for the mathematician who has not had work in linear algebras). To end, however, on a very definite problem for which a simple answer is possible, the following question is in order:

---

[5] "The Wedderburn Structure Theorems," Vol. LIV (1947), pp. 253–59.

If n-tuples of real numbers (n greater than or equal to two) are used, and if the associative law for multiplication is assumed, what algebras may be constructed having inverses (i.e., what division algebras)?

Answer: (Due to C. S. Peirce.) Only the complex numbers and the quaternions.

These are the highlights of the general theory of algebras. What are the corresponding historical landmarks? First of all, recall that a realization of the vast number of different kinds of algebras [6] did not immediately follow the invention of quaternions—even though Grassmann had some idea. For example, the British mathematician Augustus De Morgan (1806–1887), wrote as follows: "I think the time will come when double algebra [complex numbers] will be the beginner's tool; and quaternions will be where double algebra is now. The Lord only knows what will come above the quaternions."

Seeking for the persons who had the best communication line to the Lord in this respect, attention is centered now on the United States. And it is at this time, incidentally, in mathematical history that the historian first finds need for a reference to what is now perhaps the leading country in the world for mathematical research.[7] For example, Smith's *History of Mathematics* has, at the end of Volume I, a chronological table listing over two hundred names of outstanding mathematicians from 3000 B.C. to A.D. 1850. And this list contains the names of only two Americans. One of these is Benjamin Peirce (1809–1880), who began the systematic study of the classification of linear algebras that was to culminate a half century later in the structure theory just de-

---

[6] There are nine possible using just couples, twenty-seven using triples, and one hundred and twenty-eight using quadruples.

[7] The U.S.S.R. is pressing us hard in this too!

scribed. (It was his son, C. S. Peirce (1839–1914), who proved the theorem on division algebras quoted above.)

By the time the next advances were recorded, American mathematicians were no longer in the poor relation class, although a doctorate from, or a year or so of post-doctoral study at, one of the great European universities (particularly German) was still considered almost essential. E. H. Moore (1862–1932) is typical of the men who drew inspiration from the great mathematicians abroad and who returned to build up a graduate school of such a caliber as to take foreign study out of the necessity class into the luxury class. Moore, like other men previously mentioned, took to mathematics at an early age and received his B.A. at Yale in 1883 and his Ph.D. in 1885. Then, financed by one of his professors, H. A. Newton, who was deeply impressed by his abilities, Moore spent a year in Germany, first at Göttingen and then in Berlin. Returning to the United States, he began as an instructor in the academy at Northwestern University. From there he went as tutor to Yale, and in 1889 back to Northwestern as assistant professor, to be promoted in 1891 to associate professor.

In the meantime he had published several worth-while papers and was chosen in 1892 by President William Rainey Harper of the newly founded University of Chicago to be head of its department of mathematics. His success in developing a top-flight department there is well recognized. He had a profound interest in mathematics and a great gift for inspiring his colleagues and graduate students. And, conveniently for our story, the very first man whose thesis work for the doctorate was done under his supervision was L. E. Dickson—who later carried on the work of the Peirces.[8]

Leonard Eugene Dickson is best known for his brilliant

---

[8] However, Moore deserves mention here in his own right, since one of his major contributions to mathematics was the unification of similar theories through the postulational method that I have emphasized.

work in the theory of numbers, but he also made important contributions to linear algebra theory. He was born in 1874, received his B.S. from Texas in 1893, his M.A. in 1894, and his Ph.D. from Chicago in 1896. Apparently he felt that he could afford a little luxury, for even though he had studied under the peers of European mathematicians, he spent a year abroad in Leipzig and Paris. Returning to the United States, he taught in California for two years and at Texas for another before returning to Chicago in 1900 as an assistant professor. There he became a full professor in 1910, retiring in 1940.

Dickson's work shows clearly that he regarded number theory much more seriously than he did linear algebras. Thus, while he would stick tenaciously to a problem in number theory (such as the "Waring problem") and work on it for many years in order to obtain a complete solution, he wrote rather sporadically on algebras. As a result, perhaps, his work finds little place in a completely modern account of the subject today. However, he and his work did stimulate others, and the germs of many far-reaching ideas are to be found in his papers. He will be ably represented by one of his students, A. A. Albert, in the next chapter.

The work of Hamilton, Cayley, Grassmann, Peirce, and Dickson came to a culmination in the structure theorems previously described and due to J. H. M. Wedderburn. Wedderburn was born in Forfar, Scotland, in 1882. He studied at the University of Edinburgh, where he received his M.A. in 1903 and his D.Sc. in 1908. After four years as an assistant professor there, from 1905 to 1909, he came to this country to become an assistant professor at Princeton. There he remained, contributing greatly to the development of an outstanding school of mathematics in that institution and working on both linear algebras and matrices. He became a full professor in 1928, emeritus in 1940, and died two years later. The structure theories which bear his name were developed in 1907. They changed the subject of linear algebras from a collection of miscellaneous results to the status of a unified theory.

PROBLEM

Study the algebra of couples $[a, b]$ where $[a, b] + [c, d] = [a + c, b + d]$ and $[a, b] \times [c, d] = [0, a \times c]$. (By "study" is meant to find out everything you can about the multiplication in the algebra.)

Chapter 11

LAST MINUTE EDITION OF THE
ALGEBRA GAZETTE

I N a sense, this chapter is not necessary in order to fulfill
the main object of this book: to portray a development
and generalization of the concept of a number from its most
primitive beginnings to modern times. For two capital problems that are currently being worked on have already been
mentioned (the classification of nilpotent algebras and the
"linkage" problem). But while these and many other problems in associative algebra theory are still unsolved, the basic
ideas have been presented in courses and books for over a
decade so that even nonspecialists are often acquainted with
them. Nonassociative algebras, on the other hand (except
for certain special cases of them), are a much newer development. I am quite certain that the course I took on these
under Professor A. A. Albert at the University of Chicago in
1942 was the first that was ever offered—at least in this country. This newness, together with the greater complexity of
nonassociative algebras, accounts for the less extensive development of the nonassociative theory as compared to the
associative theory.

Nonassociative algebras, as the reader has no doubt already surmised, differ from associative algebras in that the
multiplication of elements need not follow the associative
law. That is, while the only fundamental assumption originally given for positive integers in Chapter 3, violated by a
general associative algebra, is the commutative law of multiplication ($a \times b = b \times a$), and the only theorems of Chap-

ter 4 that are violated are Theorems 3 and 4,[1] the elements of a nonassociative algebra do not, in general, obey the associative law for multiplication, $a \times (b \times c) = (a \times b) \times c$.

As an example of a nonassociative algebra, consider first the *Cayley* numbers. Interestingly enough, as pointed out before, this one special case was mentioned by Cayley at about the same time as quaternions were by Hamilton (*c.* 1843); and today they have been analyzed almost as thoroughly as the quaternions. There is no need to describe them in detail, and I shall simply say that they may be described as a certain set of 8-tuples, (a, b, c, d, e, f, g, h), of real numbers (or elements of a field), with a certain multiplication law quite similar to that for the quaternions. Furthermore, if the particular Cayley number $(1, 0, \cdots, 0)$ is designated by 1; $(0, 1, 0, \cdots, 0)$ by i_1; $(0, 0, 1, 0, \cdots, 0)$ by i_2; $\cdots$; $(0, 0, \cdots, 0, 1)$ by i_7; there results $i_1^2 = i_2^2 = \cdots = i_7^2 = -1$. Again there is anticommutivity,

$$i_1 \times i_2 = -i_2 \times i_1,$$

etc. This, so far, is just like the quaternions. But there are also such equations as

$$i_1 \times (i_2 \times i_4) = -(i_1 \times i_2) \times i_4$$

which violate the associative law of multiplication. However, the Cayley numbers still have, in common with the quaternions, the property that $a \times b = 0$ implies that a and /or b is zero, and it is the only algebra in eight units over the real number field which has this property.

At this point a special but quite important problem which concerns contemporary algebraists may be mentioned. It has already been stated that the only associative algebras formed from the real numbers which satisfy the property of "$a \times b = 0$ implies that a and/or b is zero" (i.e., division

---

[1] Theorem 4 is the statement that $a \times b = 0$ implies that a and/or b is equal to 0. Theorem 3 is related to Theorem 4.

algebras) are the complex numbers and the quaternions. Dropping the requirement of associativity, the existence of such an algebra in eight units has been indicated. It is not known (1951) whether or not it is possible to step to the next stage (which can be shown to be necessarily an algebra in sixteen units) and construct a division algebra using real numbers.

The second example of a nonassociative algebra is the *Jordan* [2] algebra which is used in quantum mechanics. Here the "numbers" are again matrices for which addition and scalar multiplication proceed as in the total matric algebra of Chapter 9, but for which multiplication is defined by

$$a \cdot b = a \times b + b \times a,$$

where $a \times b$ and $b \times a$ stand for the ordinary row by column matrix product defined in Chapter 9.[3] For example,

$$\begin{pmatrix} 2 & 1 \\ -1 & 4 \end{pmatrix} \cdot \begin{pmatrix} 3 & 1 \\ 2 & -1 \end{pmatrix}$$

$$= \begin{pmatrix} 2 & 1 \\ -1 & 4 \end{pmatrix} \times \begin{pmatrix} 3 & 1 \\ 2 & -1 \end{pmatrix} + \begin{pmatrix} 3 & 1 \\ 2 & -1 \end{pmatrix} \times \begin{pmatrix} 2 & 1 \\ -1 & 4 \end{pmatrix}$$

$$= \begin{pmatrix} 8 & 1 \\ 5 & -5 \end{pmatrix} + \begin{pmatrix} 5 & 7 \\ 5 & -2 \end{pmatrix} = \begin{pmatrix} 13 & 8 \\ 10 & -7 \end{pmatrix}.$$

To illustrate the nonassociativity, take the simpler matrices,

$$a = \begin{pmatrix} 1 & 0 \\ -1 & 0 \end{pmatrix}, \quad b = \begin{pmatrix} 1 & 1 \\ -1 & 1 \end{pmatrix}, \quad c = \begin{pmatrix} 1 & 1 \\ 0 & 1 \end{pmatrix},$$

---

[2] Thus named in honor of the physicist Pascual Jordan whose recent cosmological speculations were discussed in Chapter 7.

[3] Actually, ½ $(a \times b + b \times a)$—but the ½ is unimportant here. Notice that a Jordan algebra is commutative, since $a \cdot b = a \times b + b \times a = b \times a + a \times b = b \cdot a$. There are also other types of Jordan algebras. The ones considered here are what are called "special" Jordan algebras. (See Appendix.)

and calculate

$$a \cdot b = \begin{pmatrix} 1 & 0 \\ -1 & 1 \end{pmatrix} \cdot \begin{pmatrix} 1 & 1 \\ -1 & 0 \end{pmatrix}$$

$$= \begin{pmatrix} 1 & 0 \\ -1 & 0 \end{pmatrix} \times \begin{pmatrix} 1 & 1 \\ -1 & 0 \end{pmatrix} + \begin{pmatrix} 1 & 1 \\ -1 & 0 \end{pmatrix} \times \begin{pmatrix} 1 & 0 \\ -1 & 1 \end{pmatrix}$$

$$= \begin{pmatrix} 1 & 1 \\ -1 & -1 \end{pmatrix} + \begin{pmatrix} 0 & 1 \\ -1 & 0 \end{pmatrix} = \begin{pmatrix} 1 & 2 \\ -2 & -1 \end{pmatrix}.$$

Then

$$(a \cdot b) \cdot c = \left[\begin{pmatrix} 1 & 0 \\ -1 & 1 \end{pmatrix} \cdot \begin{pmatrix} 1 & 1 \\ -1 & 0 \end{pmatrix} \right] \cdot \begin{pmatrix} 1 & 1 \\ 0 & 1 \end{pmatrix}$$

$$= \begin{pmatrix} 1 & 2 \\ -2 & -1 \end{pmatrix} \cdot \begin{pmatrix} 1 & 1 \\ 0 & 1 \end{pmatrix}$$

$$= \begin{pmatrix} 1 & 2 \\ -2 & -1 \end{pmatrix} \times \begin{pmatrix} 1 & 1 \\ 0 & 1 \end{pmatrix} + \begin{pmatrix} 1 & 1 \\ 0 & 1 \end{pmatrix} \times \begin{pmatrix} 1 & 2 \\ -2 & -1 \end{pmatrix}$$

$$= \begin{pmatrix} 1 & 3 \\ -2 & -3 \end{pmatrix} + \begin{pmatrix} -1 & 1 \\ -2 & -1 \end{pmatrix} = \begin{pmatrix} 0 & 4 \\ -4 & -4 \end{pmatrix}.$$

On the other hand,

$$b \cdot c = \begin{pmatrix} 1 & 1 \\ -1 & 0 \end{pmatrix} \cdot \begin{pmatrix} 1 & 1 \\ 0 & 1 \end{pmatrix}$$

$$= \begin{pmatrix} 1 & 1 \\ -1 & 0 \end{pmatrix} \times \begin{pmatrix} 1 & 1 \\ 0 & 1 \end{pmatrix} + \begin{pmatrix} 1 & 1 \\ 0 & 1 \end{pmatrix} \times \begin{pmatrix} 1 & 1 \\ -1 & 0 \end{pmatrix}$$

$$= \begin{pmatrix} 1 & 2 \\ -1 & -1 \end{pmatrix} + \begin{pmatrix} 0 & 1 \\ -1 & 0 \end{pmatrix} = \begin{pmatrix} 1 & 3 \\ -2 & -1 \end{pmatrix},$$

so that

$$a \cdot (b \cdot c) = \begin{pmatrix} 1 & 0 \\ -1 & 1 \end{pmatrix} \cdot \left[\begin{pmatrix} 1 & 1 \\ -1 & 0 \end{pmatrix} \cdot \begin{pmatrix} 1 & 1 \\ 0 & 1 \end{pmatrix} \right]$$

$$= \begin{pmatrix} 1 & 0 \\ -1 & 1 \end{pmatrix} \cdot \begin{pmatrix} 1 & 3 \\ -2 & -1 \end{pmatrix}$$

$$= \begin{pmatrix} 1 & 0 \\ -1 & 1 \end{pmatrix} \times \begin{pmatrix} 1 & 3 \\ -2 & -1 \end{pmatrix} + \begin{pmatrix} 1 & 3 \\ -2 & -1 \end{pmatrix} \times \begin{pmatrix} 1 & 0 \\ -1 & 1 \end{pmatrix}$$

$$= \begin{pmatrix} 1 & 3 \\ -3 & -4 \end{pmatrix} + \begin{pmatrix} -2 & 3 \\ -1 & -1 \end{pmatrix} = \begin{pmatrix} -1 & 6 \\ -4 & -5 \end{pmatrix},$$

which is not equal to $(a \cdot b) \cdot c$ or

$$\begin{pmatrix} 0 & 4 \\ -4 & -4 \end{pmatrix}.$$

That is, the associative law for multiplication, $(a \cdot b) \cdot c = a \cdot (b \cdot c)$, does not hold.

Two main accomplishments have been made in the theory of nonassociative algebras to date (1951). First of all, several special types of nonassociative algebras have been analyzed in considerable detail, in particular the *Lie*[4] algebras (see Problem 2 at the end of the chapter), the *Jordan* algebras illustrated above, and the *alternative* algebras,[5] of which the Cayley numbers are an example. In the second place it has been shown that a considerable number of the properties of a nonassociative algebra are related to the properties of a certain *associative* algebra (called the *enveloping* algebra) which is connected with each nonassociative alge-

---

[4] Named after the Norwegian mathematician M. S. Lie (1842–1899).
[5] These obey a modified form of the associative law: $a \times (b \times c) = (a \times b) \times c$ if $a = c$, $b = c$, or $a = c$.

bra. But the general structure theory, such as is sketched for the associative algebras in Chapter 10, is still rather largely a question for the future.

So far, the only living mathematician entering directly into the picture has been L. E. Dickson, and he has been on the retired list for over ten years. But now comes the delicate job of selecting a roster of productive algebraists of today— unaided by historical judgment. The selection will not be too difficult, however, for I will first of all limit myself to American mathematicians in order to keep down the size of the list, and secondly, with one exception, I shall confine myself to the mention of some of the leading, currently productive, algebraists who have contributed extensively to the *particular topics discussed* here. Thus the names of individuals who have written only one or two papers on the subject are not given, and what is more important, a host of other talented algebraists who have written a great deal on parts of algebra other than linear algebra [6] will not be mentioned.

First on the list by virtue of his position in the alphabet, his pre-eminent standing in the field, and the debt that I owe him in my training, is A. A. Albert (1905–) of the University of Chicago. His *Modern Higher Algebra* was the first textbook in English on the subject, while his *Structure of Algebras* is a fundamental exposition of results in the theory of associative algebras—much of it his own work. Recently he has pioneered in the development of nonassociative algebras, both the general theory and special cases such as Jordan algebras. Among his students who have made important contributions to the subject are Richard Schafer (1918–), of the University of Pennsylvania, whose work is directly along the lines of Albert's, particularly in nonassociative

---

[6] Such as group theory, rings, representation theory, topological algebras, arithmetic of algebras, field theory, and ordered systems.

algebras,[7] and Sam Perlis (1913–   ) of Purdue University, who is responsible for a new and worth-while definition of the "radical" of an algebra and who is currently (1951) working on nilpotent algebras.

Outstanding algebraists of German birth and training who have made their home in the United States or Canada for many years are Emil Artin (1898–   ) of Princeton University, Richard Brauer (1901–   ) of the University of Michigan, and Max Zorn (1906–   ) of Indiana University. The first two men have contributed to many of the details of the structure theory of associati ve algebras that are too technical to discuss here, while the work of Zorn that is connected with the material of this book has been with alternative algebras.

The outstanding investigator of Lie algebras in this country has been Nathan Jacobson, born in Poland in 1910 but educated in the United States, of Yale University. Most of his recent work has been with "ring" theory but he and his wife, Florence, have both worked on Jordan algebras.

Then there is Gerhard Hochschild (1915–   ) of the University of Illinois, one of the several fine younger mathematicians born in Germany who completed their training in this country, and R. H. Bruck (1914–   ) of the University of Wisconsin, who has written on the general theory of nonassociative algebras.

Finally, I want to mention at least one more distinguished algebraist, even though little of his work concerns the subject matter here. For I want to take this opportunity to acknowledge a debt of inspiration and encouragement to Saunders MacLane (1909–   ) of the University of Chicago, under whom I first came in contact with modern algebra.

---

[7] One of his recent papers deals with a type of nonassociative algebra that is used in genetics. He, and this work, were featured in a December, 1947, issue of *Life* in an article on the Institute for Advanced Study, where Schafer was studying at the time.

PROBLEMS

1. Calculate the Jordan product of the matrices $\begin{pmatrix} 0 & 1 \\ 3 & 2 \end{pmatrix}$ and $\begin{pmatrix} 1 & 0 \\ 1 & 4 \end{pmatrix}$.

2. The *Lie* product of two matrices, a and b, is defined to be $a \cdot b = a \times b - b \times a$, where $a \times b$ and $b \times a$ stand for the ordinary row by column matrix product. Calculate the Lie product of the matrices above. (The set of all two-by-two matrices under this Lie multiplication forms a Lie algebra.)

Chapter 12

THE AUTHOR'S LAMENT

ALTHOUGH I have tried to give a fair and accurate picture of both the development of a mathematical concept and current work being done on it, I realize that there are many gaps, omissions, and vague statements that might be criticized by laymen and professionals alike. However, by giving references for topics incompletely developed, using such works as "roughly", "in general", etc., I may have avoided any real criticism from either side except in one respect. And that is in the attempt to describe the work of a mathematician. It is true that I have stated some problems on which mathematicians are working, but technical difficulties have prevented a precise statement of what these problems are. What is probably more important, the preceding pages give only an inkling of the vast ramifications of modern mathematics, and they enlighten the reader only a little about what justification there is, if any, for mathematicians to spend time working on these problems. This concluding chapter, then, is an attempt to shed some light on these important questions.

To give a good idea of the ramifications of modern mathematics, it may almost suffice to list the contents of an issue of the monthly *Mathematical Reviews* (that of September, 1949) which was picked at random. This important periodical gives a summary of mathematical articles and books (excluding undergraduate textbooks and articles on the teaching of mathematics) that are published throughout the world.

	NUMBER OF ARTICLES
TOPIC	OR BOOKS REVIEWED

TOPIC	NUMBER OF ARTICLES OR BOOKS REVIEWED
Foundations	10
Algebra	12
Abstract Algebra	15
Theory of Groups	18
Number Theory	48
Analysis	5
Calculus	8
Theory of Sets and Functions of Real Variables	32
Theory of Functions of Complex Variables	31
Theory of Series	5
Fourier Series and Generalizations, Integral Transforms	18
Polynomials, Polynomial Approximations	4
Special Functions	9
Harmonic Functions, Potential Theory	13
Differential Equations	43
Difference Equations, Special Functional Equations	7
Integral Equations	10
Functional Analysis, Ergodic Theory	30
Theory of Probability	14
Mathematical Statistics	17
Mathematical Economics	3
Mathematical Biology	4
Topology	26
Geometry	21
Convex Domains, Extremal Problems	7
Algebraic Geometry	18
Differential Geometry	35
Numerical and Graphical Methods	31
Astronomy	8
Relativity	19
Mathematical Physics	10
Quantum Mechanics	13
Total	544

Now if all the papers on algebra were on linear algebras, they would comprise about 5 per cent of the total. It so happens, however, that only two are, or less than ½ per cent. Allowing for differences in proportion at various times, we can safely assert that fewer than 2 per cent of papers and books today are concerned with the material discussed in the last three chapters.[1] Continuing a little further, notice that the great majority of names of sections convey nothing to the layman, nor would many of them to the undergraduate mathematics major. And even when the title appears clear enough (such as algebra and geometry), the articles reviewed certainly do not deal with what might be expected, as should be evident from a reading of this book.

What would they mean to a Ph.D. in mathematics? Clearly, that would depend on how recent a Ph.D. and how much contact he had maintained with developments since leaving graduate school, as well as on his native ability and the quality of training he had received in graduate school. An average, well-trained, recent Ph.D. would, I think, have at least a speaking acquaintance with most but not all of the topics listed. However, generally the articles reviewed in all but about half a dozen subdivisions would be unintelligible to him. In these six fields he could grasp the gist of most (but again, not all) of the articles reviewed and read perhaps 10 per cent of them with a fair degree of ease and understanding.[2]

At the extreme ends of the understanding scale, consider first an old-time Ph.D. from a minor university who has con-

---

[1] In the entire ten issues of 1949, some 6,000 papers or books were reviewed. Of these, 332, or less than 6 per cent, were classified as algebra, while 63, or slightly more than 1 per cent, were classified as dealing with associative or nonassociative algebras. The rest deal with fields, Galois theory, rings, and other topics not discussed in this book. Furthermore, many of the papers classified under associative or nonassociative algebras deal with topics concerning these subjects which were not considered here. Incidentally, not all the classifications used in the index are listed above in the tabulation of the one issue. The index uses 81 main classifications, with 341 subheadings. *Algebra: abstract* has 11 subheadings; *algebra: equations* has 5; and *algebra: linear* (*classical theory*) has 6.

[2] This figure refers to a reading from previous background alone. With a little brushing up and some preliminary study, the figure might be substantially increased.

fined himself strictly to teaching the first two years of mathematics in a junior college. He would still be able to
comprehend some of the articles reviewed, for the simple
reason that about 2 per cent of them are from the three or
four journals that deal mainly with undergraduate mathematics. But he certainly would have no idea of the meaning
of most of the articles from the real research journals. And
on the other hand, there are a half dozen or so outstanding
men whc have devoted years to research and study who
might at least understand the basic ideas behind most of the
articles reviewed and be able to evaluate them and fit them
into a general pattern of mathematical development.

Let us turn now to the second question—the justification
of the mathematician's existence. First it might be well to
point out that a large percentage of teachers of mathematics
do not develop any original mathematics at all; i.e., they are
not research mathematicians. With only a trifling number of
exceptions, no high-school teacher of mathematics carries on
original research today (in the United States—the situation
has been somewhat different abroad, where higher standards
are held for high-school work). And with no exceptions, no
high-school teacher does any research of the type which is
published in the major research journals (for example, in
this country, the *Proceedings of the American Mathematical
Society, Transactions of the American Mathematical Society,
Duke Mathematical Journal, American Journal of Mathematics,* and *Annals of Mathematics*). With a very few exceptions the same remarks may be made about instructors in
junior colleges, in teachers' colleges, and even in the small
liberal arts colleges.[3]

Now how can research activity be measured? In most
cases an accurate index is the number of pages published in

---

[3] There are several outstanding exceptions in the last group, but they are
still very much in the minority.

the journals. For there are such a small number of research mathematicians that few really advanced books are published, and those that are published are usually largely based on material that was previously issued in journals. And for reasons of personal pride, as well as because of the fact that promotions are often based on articles published, most mathematicians submit their research to journals or, at least, present the results orally at mathematics meetings.[4]

Now it is safe to say that any American with any interest in research mathematics belongs to the American Mathematical Society. The membership of this group is only about five thousand (1951), and of this small number, certainly less than half have ever contributed a paper to the society at any one of its four or more meetings a year.[5] When one begins to demand more than one paper (which might have been the man's doctoral dissertation), the number drops still further. Specifically, a survey made by R. G. D. Richardson in 1938 showed that of the six hundred and sixty-six American mathematicians taking doctor's degrees in the period 1895 to 1924,[6] 39 per cent published *no* papers and 18 per cent only *one* paper. And those publishing more than five papers numbered only 22 per cent. Finally, in order to complete the picture, there were 154 doctorates in mathematics, mathematical physics, and statistics conferred in this country and

---

[4] A *few* distinguished men publish very little. Their reputation has already been made, and they contribute many ideas to their students and the "small fry" while they work on very difficult long-term projects. Also, of course, the quality of publication is as important a consideration as the quantity.

[5] Two national meetings are held each year. Then about Thanksgiving and Easter, separate sectional meetings are held around the same time in the East, Midwest, and West. There are also occasional extra meetings for the more populous East and Midwest, and less frequent meetings of Southern and Northwestern sections.

[6] This period was selected by Richardson "as being far enough in the past so that men had an opportunity to get something into print, and not extending back far enough so that lack of publication facility and of stimulus enters into the calculation."

Canada in 1950, 139 in 1949, 121 in 1948, 102 in 1947, and 58 in 1946.[7]

The small numbers given above should convince anyone that, even if contemporary mathematics had not the slightest practical application (and the topics discussed in this book do have considerable use), it would not be an extravagant waste of man power to let these few unusual people continue their work. Although the work of individual mathematicians varies from that which is applicable tomorrow to the building of airplanes, to that which has no conceivable application even in the far distant future, let us take, in conclusion, the case of a mathematician working at the far end of the "useful" scale.

What might such a man say in justification of his career? (Not that many of them would consider bothering to justify it—they're too busy making it!) In his book, *A Mathematician's Apology*,[8] the great "pure" mathematician, G. H. Hardy (1877–1947), is content to base his case for the justification of the existence of men such as he on three points:

1. In the first place, Hardy says, a "pure" mathematician does no one any harm! This rather negative virtue is not to be ignored, however, when one considers some current work of the chemists and physicists!
2. Achievements that are performable by such a small number of people certainly deserve some recognition, regardless of their usefulness to society. We have seen how rare a productive mathematician is, and certainly, says Hardy, his achievements are as worthy of public support as the achievements of the best golfer or champion swimmer!
3. The permanence of mathematical achievement, concludes Hardy, indicates that it is worth while today. This, of

---

[7] The 1946 figure shows the influence of the war years when our short-sighted policies toward scientific personnel practically stripped the graduate schools of male students.

[8] Cambridge University Press, 1941.

Now

$$(a+d)+f = (b+c)+f \quad \text{(logical identity, since}$$
$$a+d = b+c, \; f=f),$$
$$= (b+c)+f = b+(c+f) \quad \text{(associative law of addition for positive integers),}$$
$$= b+(c+f) = b+(d+e) \quad \text{(logical identity, since}$$
$$c+f = d+e).$$

Thus

$$(a+d)+f = b+(d+e) \quad \text{(logical identity).}$$

But

$$(a+d)+f = a+(d+f) \quad \text{(associative law of addition for positive integers),}$$
$$= a+(d+f) = a+(f+d) \quad \text{(commutative law of addition for positive integers),}$$
$$= a+(f+d) = (a+f)+d \quad \text{(associative law of addition for positive integers),}$$

Hence,

$$(a+f)+d = b+(d+e) \quad \text{(logical identity).}$$

But

$$b+(d+e) = b+(e+d) \quad \text{(commutative law of addition for positive integers),}$$
$$= b+(e+d) = (b+e)+d \quad \text{(associative law of addition for positive integers).}$$

and hence

$$(a+f)+d = (b+e)+d \quad \text{(logical identity).}$$

Finally,

$$a+f = b+e \quad \text{(cancellation law for positive integers).}$$

The last two laws are discussed later.

Now *after* these laws are verified, we may then use equality for integers as we used equality (logical identity) for *positive* integers. And it is the lack of verification of these properties in the text that makes, for example, the proof of Theorem 2 incomplete. Actually, Theorem 2 follows from Definition 2 of Chapter 5, Assumption 3 for positive integers, and the transitive law for the integers which we have just proved. For we had $(a - b) + (c - d) = (a + c) - (b + d)$ (or $x = y$) and $(c - d) + (a - b) = (c + a) - (d + b)$ (or $s = t$). But $t = y$ by Assumption 3 for positive integers and the use of logical identity for positive integers. Thus we have $s = t$, $t = y$, and, hence, $s = y$ by the transitive law. Then $x = y$, $y = s$, and hence, again by the transitive law, $x = s$ or $(a - b) + (c - d) = (c - d) + (a - b)$.

The next logical gap in the text discussion occurs in the introduction of Assumption 11, since it was not made clear why that assumption needed to be included. That is, it was clear that Assumption 10 was needed, since without Assumption 10 the set of positive fractions was still a candidate for the title of positive integers. But after Assumption 10 is added, there is no such commonplace contender for the title (outside of the whole numbers, of course). There are contenders, however, which make an additional assumption necessary. One such is the algebra of two quantities, a and b, where

$$a + a = b + b = a, \quad a + b = b + a = b,$$
$$a \times a = b \times b = a, \quad a \times b = b \times a = b.$$

It may be verified that the associative, commutative, and distributive laws hold, that a is a unit element, that the cancellation laws hold, and that the principle of finite induction is valid. *But* we have *both* an x, such that $a + x = b$ ($x = b$), and a y, such that $a = b + y$ ($y = b$), contrary to Assumption 11 which states that exactly *one* of the alternatives $a = b$, $a + x = b$, and $a = b + y$ shall hold.

After a discussion of the positive integers and the concept of equality, mathematicians usually introduce an *ordering* relation in the set of positive integers defined by

(8) m is *less* than p ($m < p$) if there exists a positive integer q such that $m + q = p$.

(For example, $3 < 5$, since $3 + 2 = 5$). Certain properties of this ordering relation are then proved as, for example,

(9) $m < n$ and $n < p$ implies that $m < p$.

(As $2 < 3$ and $3 < 4$ implies $2 < 4$.)

From positive integers, the normal procedure is to go to positive fractions in a manner very similar to that indicated in the book, plus the additional detail of defining order by

$$(10) \quad \frac{a}{b} < \frac{c}{d} \text{ if } a \times d < b \times c.$$

(For example, $\frac{2}{3} < \frac{3}{4}$ because $2 \times 4 < 3 \times 3$), and of showing invariance of order and the operations under the definition of equality. That is, $\frac{a}{b} \times \frac{c}{d}$ was defined to be $\frac{a \times c}{b \times d}$. But $\frac{a}{b} = \frac{u}{v}$ if $a \times v = b \times u$, while $\frac{c}{d} = \frac{z}{y}$ if $c \times y = d \times z$. Then is $\frac{a}{b} \times \frac{c}{d}$ equal to $\frac{u}{v} \times \frac{z}{y}$? The answer is "yes", since $\frac{a}{b} \times \frac{c}{d} = \frac{a \times c}{b \times d}$, $\frac{u}{v} \times \frac{z}{y} = \frac{u \times z}{v \times y}$, and it is easy to show that $\frac{a \times c}{b \times d} = \frac{u \times z}{v \times y}$. Then, of course, addition is treated similarly via the definition $\frac{a}{b} + \frac{c}{d}$ $= \frac{a \times d + b \times c}{b \times d}$.

Now comes the big job of filling out the system of positive numbers with the irrationals. This was discussed from the Cantor viewpoint in the text. It is more often done by setting up a system of *Dedekind cuts*. Briefly, mathematicians understand by a cut [2] a method of dividing the set of all rational numbers into two classes, A and B, such that every element of class B is greater than every element of class A. For every cut there are just three possibilities, one and only one of which may hold.

(1) There is a *largest* element a^* of A. This would occur, for example, if A consisted of all rational numbers less than or equal to 1, and B consisted of all rational numbers greater than 1 (then a^* is equal to 1).

(2) There is a *smallest* element b^* of B. This would occur, for example, if A consisted of all rational numbers less than 1

---

[2] Adapted in part from Courant and Robbins (see Bibliography).

and B consisted of all rational numbers greater than or equal to 1 (then b^* is equal to 1).

(3) There is *neither* a *largest* element in A nor a *smallest* element in B. This would occur, for example, if A consisted of all rational numbers with square less than 2, and B of all rational numbers with square greater than 2. Since it was shown in Chapter 7 that the square of *no* rational number is 2, it follows that A and B together include all rational numbers. But A has no largest element, as $(1.4)^2 < 2$, $(1.41)^2 < 2$, $(1.414)^2 < 2$, $\cdots$ so that 1.4, $(<)$ 1.41, $(<)$ 1.414, $(<)$ $\cdots$ (where $\cdots$ means that one can continue indefinitely) are all in A. Similarly, B has no least element.

In this third case, the cut is said to define or simply to *be* an irrational number (as $\sqrt{2}$ in the example). Appropriate definitions for the equality of two cuts and the sum and product of two cuts follow, and the theory is completed by showing that addition of cuts is commutative and associative, the product is commutative and associative, multiplication is distributive with respect to addition, and Theorems 3 to 5 of Chapter 4 hold.

Now zero and negative numbers are introduced by a device similar to that used for fractions. For example, 0 is represented by the pair of positive numbers $[a, a]$ † (i.e., $a - a$), -1 by $[a, a+1]$ (i.e., $a - (a+1)$), etc. Then $[m, n] = [r, s]$ if $m + s = n + r$ (e.g., $[1, 2] = [3, 4]$ since $1 + 4 = 2 + 3$), while sums and products are defined by $[m, n] + [r, s] = [m + r, n + s]$ and $[m, n] \times [r, s] = [m \times r + n \times s, m \times s + n \times r]$, respectively. For example, $[1, 2] + [1, 2] = [1+1, 2+2] = [2, 4]$, or $(-1) + (-1) = (-2)$, while $[1, 2] \times [1, 2] = [1 \times 1 + 2 \times 2, 1 \times 2 + 2 \times 1] = [5, 4]$, or $(-1) \times (-1) = (+1)$.

At this point let us prove the invariance of addition under our definition of equality. That is, we wish to show that if $[a, b] = [a', b']$ and $c, d = [c', d']$, we have $[a, b] + [c, d] = [a', b'] + [c', d']$. (This is our fourth requirement for equality.) This is true, since $[a, b] = [a', b']$ implies that $a' + b = b' + a$, $[c, d] = [c', d']$ implies that $c' + d = d' + c$, and hence

---

† A bracket is used here instead of a parenthesis to prevent confusion with the "complex" couple of Chapter 8. Thus $[a, b]$ is what was written a-b in Chapter 5.

$$(a' + c') + (b + d) = (b' + d') + (a + c).$$

Thus

$$[a', b'] + [c', d'] = [a' + c', b' + d'] = [a + c, b + d].$$

Similarily, the fact that "equals multiplied by equals are equal" may be checked. (The computation is somewhat more involved and will be omitted here.)

The complex numbers are then brought in as was done in Chapter 8 by the use of the couple device and an *algebraically closed* set of numbers is obtained. The word *closed* stems from the fact (mentioned in Chapter 8) that no further inventions are needed in the way of numbers in order to solve polynomial equations. More precisely now, Gauss' result [3] may be stated as:

Every polynomial equation of positive degree with complex coefficients has a complex root.

The treatment of quaternions and matrices in Chapter 9, so far as it goes, needs no amplification here except to supply the motivation for the definition of the multiplication of matrices promised there. To do this, imagine that we have given to us the linear transformation defined by

$$(1) \qquad \left. \begin{array}{l} x' = 2x + 5y \\ y' = -x - 5y \end{array} \right\}, \quad \text{matrix} \begin{pmatrix} 2 & 5 \\ -1 & -5 \end{pmatrix},$$

followed by a second transformation,

$$(2) \qquad \left. \begin{array}{l} x'' = 2x' + 3y' \\ y'' = x' + 4y' \end{array} \right\}, \quad \text{matrix} \begin{pmatrix} 2 & 3 \\ 1 & 4 \end{pmatrix}.$$

Substituting from (1) for x' and y' in (2), we have

$$\left. \begin{array}{l} x'' = 2 (2x + 5y) + 3 (-x - 5y) \\ \quad = 4x + 10y - 3x - 15y = x - 5y \\ \\ y'' = (2x + 5y) + 4 (-x - 5y) \\ \quad = 2x + 5y - 4x - 20y = -2x - 15y \end{array} \right\}, \quad \text{matrix} \begin{pmatrix} 1 & -5 \\ -2 & -15 \end{pmatrix}.$$

---

[3] Once known as the "Fundamental Theorem of Algebra". It still is—for this *branch* of algebra!

Our desired motivation then comes from noting that the matrix of the new transformation is precisely the product (as shown in Chapter 9), $\begin{pmatrix} 2 & 3 \\ 1 & 4 \end{pmatrix} \times \begin{pmatrix} 2 & 5 \\ -1 & -5 \end{pmatrix}$, of the first two matrices. (And this was Cayley's motivation too.)

In Chapter 10 a large number of terms were left partially or completely undefined, such as linear algebra itself, total matric algebra, nilpotent algebra, sum of algebras, direct sum of algebras, direct product of algebras, semi-simple algebras, and simple algebras. I shall not, however, attempt to remedy this situation here. For in the first place, the central point of the chapter— namely, the breaking down of a general algebra into elementary parts—can be well understood and appreciated without an understanding of these highly technical words. In the second place, a host of other concepts of algebra must be explained before the usual definitions can make sense.

Lest the reader think that I am just being lazy about this, consider the definition of a *simple* algebra (that ought to be simple!):

A simple algebra is an algebra whose only proper ideal is the zero ideal and that is not a zero algebra of order one.

No, this is not a joke—but I do not use the words "proper ideal" to describe the moral state of the algebra! First of all, by an *ideal,* the algebraist means:

A subset B of an algebra A such that b and b' in B implies that $b - b'$ is in B, and a in A implies that both $a \times b$ and $b \times a$ are in B for every b in B and every a in A.

Then a *proper* ideal of A is an ideal which does not consist of all the elements of A. Finally, a *zero* algebra of order one is the set of all 1-tuples (a) such that $(a)^2 = (0)$.

Clearly, all this (assuming the concept of a *subset* is self-evident) is meaningless without considerable preliminaries and a careful study of examples. In other words, if the reader wants to get a better understanding of the material of Chapters 10 and 11, he will have to return to a study of the more basic concepts of the number system and its generalizations. For there is no more of a royal road to algebra than there is to geometry, and I must confess that I, like all other popularizers of mathematics, have only led the reader to a comparatively easily reached vantage point where he can gaze at the majestic pinnacles of mathematical achievement. But, in order actually to scale these peaks, he must go back and take the regular trails—inspired, I hope, by the view that he has seen!

Finally, concerning Chapter 11, I should point out that the general Jordan algebra is defined as one for which the special form of the associative law, $a \times (b \times a^2) = (a \times b) \times a^2$ holds, while a Lie algebra is one in which $a \times (b \times c) + b \times (c \times a) + c \times (a \times b) = 0$.

course, is the same sort of argument that may be applied to the classics of literature and the arts.

Personally, I do not find these arguments very convincing. I should like to add three more justifications.

First, with almost no exception, even the top research men in mathematics do some teaching, and the spark of enthusiasm that they may kindle in some student by reason of their own keen interest in mathematics may grow into a bonfire of achievement by the student in some other, more practical, line of mathematics. This to me is the most potent reason for some research activity on the part of as many teachers as possible.

Secondly, mathematics, although extremely and intricately diversified, still possesses a deep underlying unity. Thus, although a certain discovery may have no direct application at any time, it may, in devious ways, come to influence a branch of mathematics which has practical applications. This is not uncommon.

Finally, the abstract mathematics of today may become the practical mathematics of tomorrow. In the seventeenth and eighteenth centuries perhaps most mathematical research was directly inspired by a need for mathematics in the sciences. Today, however, mathematics is largely a self-perpetuating subject. In some branches it still draws inspiration from physics, astronomy, etc., but on the whole it has far surpassed the current need for mathematical tools in these subjects.[9] But who can tell what mathematical tools the physical, biological, and social sciences of twenty years hence will need?

Perhaps relatively few mathematicians have ever stopped to justify their own work in this fashion. All they know is

---

[9] This remark needs qualification. On the one hand it is true that an enormous amount of mathematics has been developed for which, at present, there is no application. But on the other hand, there definitely are many physical problems crying for solution for which mathematicians have as yet developed no tools.

that they find the development of mathematics to be an extremely absorbing occupation for which they are peculiarly adapted. For details of the personalities of some of these gifted men, in addition to the sketches presented, the reader is referred to E. T. Bell's *Men of Mathematics.* As pointed out there, mathematicians range over the whole spectrum in politics, religious beliefs, and philosophy of life. They may not even agree as to their own view of mathematics, although Bell believes that most would be in harmony with the famous statement of Bertrand Russell:

Mathematics, rightly viewed, possesses not only truth but supreme beauty—a beauty cold and austere, like that of sculpture, without appeal to any part of our weaker nature, without the gorgeous trappings of painting or music, yet sublimely pure, and capable of a stern perfection such as only the greatest art can show. The true spirit of delight, the exaltation, the sense of being more than man, which is the touchstone of the highest excellence, is to be found in mathematics as surely as in poetry.

APPENDIX

The purpose of this section is to describe, with utmost brevity, the line of approach that might [1] be taken in a series of formal courses on the subject matter of this book. This will enable those readers who have some thought of going on to orientate themselves with respect to the "professional" viewpoint.

From this point of view, the material of the first two chapters, although essential as background material here, does not enter into the picture. Instead, the mathematician begins by considering a set of undefined positive integers (as in Chapter 3). Then he postulates the existence of what is called the *successor* function, $S(n)$. His assumptions about the successor function and the positive integers are:

(1) 1 is an integer.
(2) Every integer, n, has a unique number, $S(n)$, as its successor.
(3) No integer has 1 as its successor.
(4) $S(n) = S(m)$ implies $n = m$.
(5) The principle of finite induction is valid (our Assumption 10).

(These are the *Peano* postulates mentioned in Chapter 3.)

Thus *one* unspecified operation (function) is associated with the integers instead of the *two* of Chapter 3. Then addition and multiplication can be *defined* in terms of $S(n)$ as follows:

(6) $n + 1 = S(n)$, $n + S(m) = S(n+m)$.
(7) $n \times 1 = n$, $n \times S(m) = n \times m + n$.

From (1) to (7), Assumptions 1 to 7 of Chapter 3 and 8 to 11 of Chapter 4 can be *proved*.

Now in these postulates we are considering equality as logical identity and we need not discuss it further. In the work of later

---

[1] More than one approach is possible.

chapters, however, we *define* equality of new types of numbers (as signed numbers and fractions) on the basis of the equality (logical identity) of positive integers. It turns out, then, that in order for this defined equality to be "useful" it must have certain properties, as follows:

The reflexive law: For any a, $a = a$.

The symmetric law: If $a = b$, then $b = a$.

The transitive law (things equal to the same thing are equal to each other): If $a = b$ and $b = c$, then $a = c$.

Equals added to equals give equals: If $a = c$ and $b = d$, then $a + b = c + d$.

Equals multiplied by equals give equals: If $a = c$ and $b = d$, then $a \times b = c \times d$.

Let us see whether or not the definition of equality made for the pairs $a - b$ satisfies these requirements. Recall that we said that

$$a - b = c - d \quad \text{if} \quad a + d = b + c.$$

Then is

(a) $a - b = a - b$? (The reflexive law.)

Yes, because $a + b = b + a$ (the commutative law of addition for positive integers).

(b) If $a - b = c - d$, does $c - d = a - b$? (The symmetric law.)

Yes, because if $a + d = b + c$, then $c + b = d + a$ (the commutative law of addition for positive integers and logical identity).

(c) If $a - b = c - d$ and $c - d = e - f$, does $a - b = e - f$? (The transitive law.)

Yes, because if $a - b = c - d$, $a + d = b + c$, and if $c - d = e - f$, then $c + f = d + e$. Thus from $a + d = b + c$ and $c + f = d + e$, we wish to prove that $a + f = b + e$ (since this is the condition that $a - b = e - f$). That is,

Given: $a + d = b + c$, $c + f = d + e$.

To prove: $a + f = b + e$.

SUGGESTIONS FOR FURTHER READING

First of all I list several histories of mathematics:

Archibald, R. C. *Outline of the History of Mathematics*. Menasha (Wis.): Mathematical Association of America, 1949.

Bell, E. T. *The Development of Mathematics* (2nd edition). New York: McGraw-Hill Book Co., Inc., 1945.

Cajori, Florian. *History of Mathematics*. New York: The Macmillan Co., 1919.

Sanford, Vera. *A Short History of Mathematics*. Boston: Houghton Mifflin Co., 1930.

Smith, David E. *History of Mathematics* (Vols. 1 and 2). Boston: Ginn & Co., 1923, 1925.

All except Bell's are standard works. That of Smith is the most detailed; Sanford deals only with elementary mathematics; Archibald is short but authoritative and it corrects many errors found in earlier works. While unconventional, Bell's book is particularly recommended. He is concerned not with recording as many events in mathematical history as possible, but with presenting and explaining the high lights. It is the only book of the five which gives serious consideration to twentieth-century mathematics.

Other noteworthy works by Bell are *The Magic of Numbers* (New York: McGraw-Hill Book Co., Inc., 1946) and *Men of Mathematics* (New York: Simon & Schuster, Inc., 1940). The first-named book, his most recent, is a detailed exposition of the Pythagorean position (see Chapter 7) in ancient and modern times, while the second is a series of brilliantly written biographies of outstanding mathematicians from Archimedes (287?–212 B.C.) to Georg Cantor (1845–1918), together with an excellent exposition of their ideas. In connection with the topics of this book, see, in particular, Chapter 14, "The Prince of Mathematicians" (Gauss); Chapter 16, "The Copernicus of Geometry" (Lobachevsky); Chapter 19, "An Irish Tragedy" (Hamilton); Chapter 21, "Invariant Twins" (Sylvester and Cayley); Chapter 23, "Complete Independence" (George Boole); and Chapter 25, "The Doubter" (Kronecker).

For Chapters 1 and 2, the classic works are those of L. L. Conant, *The Number Concept* (New York: The Macmillan Co., 1923) and

David E. Smith and Louis C. Karpinski, *The Hindu-Arabic Numbers* (Boston: Ginn & Co., 1911). Less detailed and less technical is an excellent book by Tobias Dantzig, *Number, the Language of Science* (New York: The Macmillan Co., 1945).

For the increasingly complex material beyond Chapter 2, the most elementary reference is *Higher Algebra for the Undergraduate* by Marie J. Weiss (New York: John Wiley & Sons, Inc., 1949). Although this is a standard textbook for an introductory course in modern algebra, much of the material is within the range of comprehension of a mature individual, even without an extensive mathematical background. See, in particular, the following chapters: 1, "The Integers"; 2, "Rational, Real, and Complex Numbers"; 4, "Rings, Integral Domains, and Fields"; 6, "Matrices Over a Field"; and 8, "Groups, Rings, and Ideals". It also contains references for reading along more technical lines. On a slightly more advanced level, there is *A Survey of Modern Algebra* by Garrett Birkhoff and Saunders MacLane (New York: The Macmillan Co., 1941).

Finally, I mention two excellent books on general mathematics whose aims, in general, are the same as those of this present volume. These are, *Mathematics and the Imagination* by Edward Kasner and James Newman (New York: Simon & Schuster, Inc., 1940) and *What Is Mathematics?* by Richard Courant and Herbert E. Robbins (New York: Oxford University Press, 1941). The first of these is delightfully humorous and not at all technical, but it does not deal directly with the materials discussed here. The second demands a certain amount of background—at least that of a good course in high-school algebra. Chapters 1 and 2, on the real number system, are the ones that apply to the discussion in this present volume.

Other good references could be given, but by consulting any of the books named above the reader will find other bibliographies to carry him further along in whatever phase of the subject he finds most interesting.

ANSWERS TO PROBLEMS

CHAPTER 1

ome, do, tee, fur, fit, fit-ome, fit-do, fit-tee, fit-fur, do fit, do fit-ome, do fit-do, do fit-tee, do fit-fur, tee fit, tee fit-ome, tee fit-do, tee fit-tee, tee fit-fur, fur fit, fur fit-ome, fur fit-do, fur fit-tee, fur fit-fur, hud (one to twenty-five in the decimal system).

CHAPTER 2

1. $12 = 1 \times 10 + 2 \times 1 = 2 \times 5 + 2 \times 1$. Hence $(12)_{10} = (22)_5$ (where the subscript refers to the base). Or, in the letter system introduced in Chapter 2, $12 = bb$.

2. $(12)_{10} = 1 \times 2^3 + 1 \times 2^2 + 0 \times 2 + 0 \times 1$. Hence $(12)_{10} = (1100)_2$.

3. $apc = 1 \times 5^2 + 0 \times 5 + 3 \times 1 = 25 + 0 + 3 = (28)_{10}$.

4. $(10101)_2 = 1 \times 2^4 + 0 \times 2^3 + 1 \times 2^2 + 0 \times 2 + 1 \times 1 = 16 + 0 + 4 + 0 + 1 = (21)_{10}$.

5.
$$apc = 1 \times 5^2 + 0 \times 5 + 3 \times 1 = 28$$
$$bd = 2 \times 5 + 4 \times 1 = 14$$
$$\overline{acb = 1 \times 5^2 + 3 \times 5 + 2 \times 1 = 42}$$

$c + d = ab$. Put down the b and carry a. Then $a + p + b = a + b = c$.

CHAPTER 3

1. For odd numbers, Assumption 1 does not hold, since the sum of two odd numbers is not odd but even. But the product of two odd numbers is again odd, so that Assumption 2 does hold. Since both the sum and the product of two even numbers are even, Assumptions 1 and 2 both hold for the set of even numbers.

2. It does not. For example, if a is the sentence, "I love Mary", and b is the sentence, "Search the thief", $a + b$ is "I the Mary". Even our freshman composition students would, I think, refuse to call "$a + b$" a sentence!

3. No! $a + b$ is the sentence, "I hate Mary", while $b + a$ is the sentence, "You love Mary".

4. The part which is covered by both the horizontal and the vertical lines is $a \times (b + c)$. The part which is covered by both the horizon-

tal and vertical lines is $a \times b$, while the part which is covered by both horizontal and slant lines is $a \times c$.

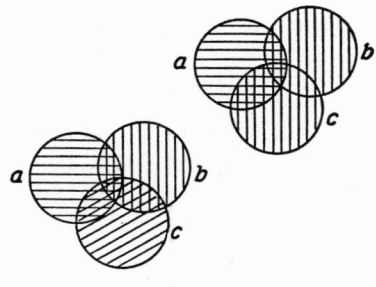

Hence $a \times (b + c) = a \times b + a \times c$.

5. $2 \oplus 3 = 2^2 + 3^2 = 4 + 9 = 13$, $(2 \oplus 3) \oplus 4 = 13 \oplus 4 = 13^2$ $+ 4^2 = 169 + 16 = 185$. On the other hand, $3 \oplus 4 = 3^2 + 4^2 = 9$ $+ 16 = 25$, $2 \oplus (3 \oplus 4) = 2 \oplus 25 = 2^2 + 25^2 = 4 + 625 = 629$. Hence $(2 \oplus 3) \oplus 4 = 185 \neq 629 = 2 \oplus (3 \oplus 4)$.

6.

STEPS	REASON
1. Let $c + d = e$ — another integer	Assumption 1
2. $a \times [b + (c + d)] = a \times (b + e)$	Equals for equals
3. $a \times (b + e) = a \times b + a \times e$	Assumption 7
4. $a \times b + a \times e = a \times b + a \times (c + d)$	Equals for equals
5. $a \times b + a \times (c + d) = a \times b + (a \times c + a \times d)$	Assumption 7

$$Q.E.D.$$

CHAPTER 4

In symbols, we have

+	a	b		×	a	b
a	a	b		a	a	a
b	b	a		b	a	b

Of course we have closure, since the only entries in the table are a and b. Secondly, $a + b = b + a = b$, $a \times b = b \times a = a$ so that we have commutativity for both addition and multiplication. To check associativity we have

$$a + (a + b) = a + b = b, \quad (a + a) + b = a + b = b;$$
$$a + (b + b) = a + a = a, \quad (a + b) + b = b + b = a;$$
$$a \times (a \times b) = a \times a = a, \quad (a \times a) \times b = a \times b = a;$$
$$a \times (b \times b) = a \times b = a, \quad (a \times b) \times b = a \times b = a.$$

CHAPTER 9

1. $(0, 1, 1, 1) + (1, 0, 2, 3) = (0 + 1, 1 + 0, 1 + 2, 1 + 3) = (1, 1, 3, 4)$.

2. $(0, 1, 1, 1) \times (1, 0, 2, 3) = (0 \times 1 - 1 \times 0 - 1 \times 2 - 1 \times 3, 0 \times 0 + 1 \times 1 + 1 \times 3 - 1 \times 2, 0 \times 2 + 1 \times 1 + 1 \times 0 - 1 \times 3, 0 \times 3 + 1 \times 2 + 1 \times 1 - 1 \times 0) = (0 - 0 - 2 - 3, 0 + 1 + 3 - 2, 0 + 1 + 0 - 3, 0 + 2 + 1 - 0) = (-5, 2, -2, 3)$.

3. $\begin{pmatrix} 0 & 1 \\ 3 & 2 \end{pmatrix} + \begin{pmatrix} 1 & 0 \\ 1 & 4 \end{pmatrix} = \begin{pmatrix} 1 & 1 \\ 4 & 6 \end{pmatrix}$.

4. $\begin{pmatrix} 0 & 1 \\ 3 & 2 \end{pmatrix} \times \begin{pmatrix} 1 & 0 \\ 1 & 4 \end{pmatrix} = \begin{pmatrix} 0 \times 1 + 1 \times 1 & 0 \times 0 + 1 \times 4 \\ 3 \times 1 + 2 \times 1 & 3 \times 0 + 2 \times 4 \end{pmatrix}$

$= \begin{pmatrix} 0 + 1 & 0 + 4 \\ 3 + 2 & 0 + 8 \end{pmatrix} = \begin{pmatrix} 1 & 4 \\ 5 & 8 \end{pmatrix}$.

CHAPTER 10

The "units" (as $1, i, j, k$ in the quaternions) are $(1, 0) = u$, $(0, 1) = v$. Then $(1, 0) \times (1, 0) = (0, 1 \times 1) = (0, 1)$, (i.e., $u^2 = v$); $(1, 0) \times (0, 1) = (0, 1) \times (1, 0) = (0, 1) \times (0, 1) = (0, 0)$, (i.e., $u \times v = v \times u = v^2 = 0$). Thus the multiplication table of units is

$\times$	u	v
u	v	0
v	0	0

This is the simplest example of a nilpotent algebra that is not a "zero" algebra, that is, one with *all* products zero.

CHAPTER 11

1. $\begin{pmatrix} 0 & 1 \\ 3 & 2 \end{pmatrix} \cdot \begin{pmatrix} 1 & 0 \\ 1 & 4 \end{pmatrix} = \begin{pmatrix} 0 & 1 \\ 3 & 2 \end{pmatrix} \times \begin{pmatrix} 1 & 0 \\ 1 & 4 \end{pmatrix} +$

$\begin{pmatrix} 1 & 0 \\ 1 & 4 \end{pmatrix} \times \begin{pmatrix} 0 & 1 \\ 3 & 2 \end{pmatrix} = \begin{pmatrix} 1 & 4 \\ 5 & 8 \end{pmatrix} + \begin{pmatrix} 0 & 1 \\ 12 & 9 \end{pmatrix} = \begin{pmatrix} 1 & 5 \\ 17 & 17 \end{pmatrix}$.

2. $\begin{pmatrix} 0 & 1 \\ 3 & 2 \end{pmatrix} \cdot \begin{pmatrix} 1 & 0 \\ 1 & 4 \end{pmatrix} = \begin{pmatrix} 1 & 4 \\ 5 & 8 \end{pmatrix} - \begin{pmatrix} 0 & 1 \\ 12 & 9 \end{pmatrix} = \begin{pmatrix} 1 & 3 \\ -7 & -1 \end{pmatrix}$.

INDEX